Relax!

A Happy
Business Story

Relax!

A Happy
Business Story

―――――

by
Henry Stewart
Cathy Busani
James Moran

First published in Great Britain 2009 By Happy
40 Adler Street, London E1 EE

A complete catalogue record of this book can be obtained from the British
Library on request.

ISBN: 978-0-9561986-0-0

The right of Henry Stewart, Cathy Busani and James Moran to be identified
as the authors of this work has been asserted by them in accordance with the
Copyright, Designs and Patents Act 1988.

We would love you to reproduce this work, in full or in part. Please feel free to
do so, providing you acknowledge the copyright of Happy Computers as part
of any reproduction. Please also send details of where you have reproduced it to
relax@happy.co.uk.

Typeset by Martin Worthington

Contents

About This Book

If you are reading this book, it means you want to make your work environment a better place. Maybe you're the manager, maybe the owner, or an employee who wants things to change – everyone can learn something from this. It won't tell you what to do, or what to think. It will tell you a story instead. Some of the things in the story are true. Some things, we would like to be true. But they are all ideas that we fully believe will improve any workplace. Maybe we're right, maybe not. We don't pretend to have all the answers, and we certainly don't think that everything we say is absolutely right. If you think some of these ideas will work for you, give them a try. If you are not sure, give them a try anyway. What have you got to lose, apart from your old ways of working?

Many ideas in this book come from how we do things at our company, Happy (previously known as Happy Computers). However, none of the companies mentioned are based specifically on our workplace – we're still learning, like you. Although we are only small (around 50 staff) we have received wide recognition for our unique culture, including being rated the best company in the country for customer service by *Management Today* and one of the two best workplaces in the UK by the *Financial Times*. The company's awards include:

- *Financial Times* Best Workplaces: Top 20 in UK in 2004, 2006, 2007 & 2008 (2nd place in 2007)
- Best Small Business in UK for Impact on Society 2006 (Business in the Community)
- Most Inspired Workplace Award 2005 (Inspired Leaders Network)
- Best in UK for work/life balance 2004 *(Financial Times)*
- Best in UK for customer service 2003 *(Management Today/*Unisys Service Excellence awards)
- IT Training Company of the Year: Gold 2001, 2009; Silver 2006, 2007, 2008; Bronze 2002, 2003, 2004

Happy was originally solely an IT training company, seeking to make learning about computers an involving and fun experience. Our fastest growing division now is Happy People, which helps companies create great workplaces.

If you would like to know more about us, or if we can help you create a great workplace, then we would love to hear from you:

Happy Ltd
Cityside House
40 Adler Street
London E1 1EE
020 7375 7300
happy@happy.co.uk

Or contact Henry directly on henry@happy.co.uk

March 2009

About The Authors

Henry Stewart is the founder and Chief Executive of Happy. He set up the company in his back room in Hackney in 1990, after a series of less-than-great experiences working for others.

Cathy Busani is Managing Director of Happy and is responsible for all the people stuff. She has been rated one of the best half-dozen bosses in the UK in two separate awards: one run by Lloyds and the DTI (Department of Trade & Industry) in 2001 and one by the *Daily Telegraph* in 2006.

James Moran worked for Happy as a content writer from 2001 to 2008. He is now a professional scriptwriter. His work includes the film *Severance* and scripts for *Dr Who* and *Torchwood*.

Prologue

I should have been having fun. I really should. Sun, sand, sea, my wife, my kids, a beautiful villa right on the beach, just down from a bar that did great lobster – I should have been having the time of my life.

But I wasn't.

I was trying to talk to my sales manager on my mobile, which was heating up in my hand so fast I thought it was going to explode at any second. The sound kept cutting out, and I kept having to say "Sorry? Sorry? Hello?" like some sort of demented parrot; my kids were crying because Daddy wouldn't build them a sandcastle; and I was getting a nasty patch of sunburn on my stomach. In short, it wasn't going well.

Just down the beach a little way, there was some guy playing frisbee with his kids. Not a care in the world, he clearly didn't have a major multinational company to worry about. He'd probably won the holiday in a competition or something. I hoped he would fall over and get sand in his shorts.

"Hello?" I said, for the millionth time. "Hello?" Hannah, my youngest, was tugging on my shorts to get my attention, and I'd just about had enough. "Stop that! Daddy's talking work now! Go and play with your brother." That was a mistake. She started crying. Helen gave me a frosty look, and swept the kids away with her into the villa. I was alone on the beach, with my phone, and the other family. To top it all off, the signal finally gave up, and cut out. I swore, and threw the phone into the sea, then instantly regretted it. I slumped down onto the beach.

The other guy's frisbee landed near my head, spraying sand, and he came running over.

"Sorry mate," he said, cheerfully. "You all right? You look a bit stressed."

"Stressed? What would you know about stress?" I snapped.

"Ooh, lots. I know how to get rid of it, for a start."

"Yeah? Tell me one way."

"Don't take your mobile phone on holiday with you."

I laughed, then remembered just how much I had paid for my top of the line model. I put my head in my hands and sighed.

"Easier said than done. I'm the boss of my department, I have to keep in touch."

"Well I'm the boss of my department, and I don't need to phone them up while I'm on holiday and they don't phone me."

I stared at him. He didn't look like he was a boss. Healthy, tanned, relaxed – young...

"Yeah, well, my company's probably bigger than yours. It's TripleX. You've probably heard of it." I sat back, smug. That'd impress him.

It didn't.

"TripleX? Not bad. I'm with Quad4."

I felt my mouth open, and closed it quickly. Quad4 was easily twice the size of TripleX.

"So how do you do it? How do you manage to stay so calm? How do you manage not to phone them every day?"

"It's not a big secret, but you have to be willing to change the way you run things."

"How?"

"What would your company be like if you completely trusted everybody?"

> ## What would your organisation be like if you completely trusted everyone?

"What do you mean?"

"Suppose you didn't have to keep following everyone around, telling them what to do and looking over their shoulder?"

"But they won't get any work done if I don't!"

"They will. You have to trust them to do their job."

"Trust them to do their job? I can't even trust them with the stationery, we have to keep it locked away, otherwise they'll walk off with it."

"But what if they need a pen, or a notebook?"

"They fill out a stationery requisition form, get it signed by their manager, send it to me, I approve it, then the finance manager goes and gets the pen."

"Doesn't the finance manager have anything better to do?"

"Well, yes, but she's the only one I can trust with the key."

"Right, well, when you get back, the first thing you need to do is unlock the cupboard. Nobody wants to fill out fifteen forms to get a pencil."

"It's only one form... signed three times..."

"How much time is wasted, just getting someone a pen? Wouldn't it be better if they could just get up, walk over and grab one?"

"Yeah, but what else would they grab?"

"Trust them. Sure, some people will take six notebooks home, but others will be careful. It all balances out. In the meantime, they feel like they're being treated as adults, and don't have to waste so much time."

"And that'll make everything better?"

"That's just the start. If you really want to know more, I'll tell you how we do it. Give us a call when we get back, and I'll tell you all about it."

"When we get back? Why not tell me now?"

He smiled.

"Because I'm on holiday. See you."

And with that he scrawled his contact number on the corner of my notebook and then strolled off back to his kids, throwing the frisbee back to them. I watched him go, and for a minute I actually seriously considered taking him up on his offer.

No filling out forms? People wandering around trusted, happy in their jobs, working together in peace and harmony?

Nah. Load of old rubbish. Certainly not the sort of thing you want to encourage in a proper business.

I waded into the sea to try to retrieve my mobile...

- 🐾 What would your organisation be like if you completely trusted everybody?
- 🐾 What would you have to do to get to that point?

Chapter 1

About Trust
and Information

When I got back to work, I fully expected things to be even worse than they had been before I left. While the cat's away, the mice will turn up late, fiddle their expenses and do sloppy work. How could I possibly trust that lot? I couldn't even turn my back on them for a minute.

But I was pleasantly surprised to see that things were going really well. Everyone was working longer hours than before, staying later and later to get the job done – now that's commitment. The atmosphere was quiet, intense; you could tell that people were working really hard. It was a great feeling, popping my head out of the office door at 7 p.m., and seeing everybody still there – well, except Mina; she had to leave at 5 p.m. to look after her kids. I understood that she needed to be with her family, but I knew that when promotions and pay rises came around, she would be behind other people in the queue, people who put the hours in.

After a few weeks, it started getting hard on my home life, as I was also doing the longer hours – but it was important, I had to put the work in to get the results. Sometimes we'd all go to the pub after work to relax. I had to admit, some nights I preferred that to going home. Domestic life was getting a bit strained. Helen didn't seem to understand the difficulties we were facing at work; I needed to be there. It was an intense, busy period. Then again, it always was. Luckily my people were up to the challenge.

Everyone was pulling together – we were really working as a team.

And then, for some reason, we lost two big contracts on the same day, which threw me. I heard about the first one as soon as I walked in the door one morning, everyone was talking about it. The mood in the office wasn't good. Still, I thought, at least we had a good chance of getting the other one...

But we didn't. Yasmin got stuck with the job of telling me – she'd taken the phone call, and nobody else wanted to be the bearer of bad news. Yasmin was a very good worker, but really, really quiet and shy. She would never dare to speak out on anything in meetings, but when coaxed, always came up with the cleverest ideas. She could have gone really far if she'd had a bit more confidence in herself.

She quietly crept into my office, and tried to break it to me gently. She did a good job, but the news wasn't ever going to make me happy. I asked her if they had given a reason for not going with us. She seemed hesitant to tell me, but eventually spilled the beans.

"They said we were too slow to reply to the tender," she said, nervously. "They said that they needed a more responsive company."

"Responsive? Why did we take so long to reply, then?"

"I don't know. Sorry. I mean, I understand you needed to take it on holiday to check over, and..." She trailed off when I glared at her. I hoped she wasn't suggesting it was my fault.

"Hmm. Did they mention anything else?"

"Yes – they said they were disappointed that we weren't a bit more flexible in our tender. That's the big buzz word now, apparently. Flexibility."

"Well, that's ridiculous," I blustered. "We're running a business here, we can't bend over backwards and change the way we do things just to please them. Did you tell them that?"

"Er, no, they didn't seem too interested. I think they just wanted to get me off the phone, to be honest."

The tender had taken ages to do – I'd had to check and double check everyone's work on it, to make sure there were no mistakes. The trouble was, I'd been a couple of days late getting it back to them. I mean, I'm not a miracle worker, I can only do so much at one time.

Suddenly, Ade, the sales manager, stormed into my office to find out what had happened.

"What's going on? Why did we lose the Jefferson contract?"

"What? I don't know, it's not my fault."

"Well, whose fault is it, then?"

"Somebody else's."

"Why did you hang on to the tender for so long? You knew we had to get it in quickly."

That was when I blew up at him. Very unprofessional conduct, I know, but he had to remember that I was the boss here.

"They ALL have to be in quickly! I have to go through every single tender, report, and client summary before it leaves this place, and it doesn't get any easier. Everything needs to be done yesterday. I just have to cope with it."

"Why do you have to do every single tender? Why can't somebody else help out?"

"Are you joking? I can't trust that lot with anything, never mind a complicated tender. If I don't check it, it won't be done right."

And there it was. If I didn't check it, it wouldn't be done right. But if I did check it, it wouldn't be done on time. Ade just threw his hands up in the air, and walked out in a huff. Yasmin had gone white. She crept out, trying not to make any noise.

I thought back again to the odd stranger from the beach, banging on about trusting people. Maybe if we trusted the sales staff with the occasional tender, we could – no, no, that was the road that led to disaster and mayhem. There must be something else we could do to sort this out. This really wasn't the time to start experimenting with strange ideas, though, the business was in too much trouble.

I sat back in my chair, deflated and tired. I picked up the latest copy of *MoveIt*, the industry magazine. If I read for a while, maybe had a coffee, then I could relax and forget about our woes for a bit.

But then I saw the front page article, and sat bolt upright. Quad4 had just won a major contract with Rhueven Training – not one of the ones we'd been after, otherwise I'd have been even more disheartened. There was the grinning stranger from the beach, with loads of his grinning colleagues, shaking hands with some grinning new client. I stuck my tongue out at them. They just grinned back. I read the article, and moaned quietly at the huge numbers involved. When I got to the last sentence, I slowly placed my head against the desk, and tapped it against the wood several times. It read: "Martinson, MD of Rhueven, said, 'We are delighted to award the contract to Quad4. They are an exciting, forward-thinking company. Their responsiveness and flexibility were a major factor in winning the tender.'"

And so that day, in a moment of madness, I decided to give it a go. Why not? The crazy stranger seemed to know what he was talking about, unless he was lying, and just enjoyed destroying companies with silly ideas. But the grinning faces on the cover of *MoveIt* didn't make it look as if Quad4 was run by a bunch of weirdos – rather, it did, but weirdos who knew what they were talking about. And let's face it, things couldn't really get much worse in my building.

So I gave it a go. I announced that from now on, the stationery cupboard was to be left unlocked, and that the forms no longer had to be filled in. I also abandoned the traditional way we approached new clients. Typically, the sales staff would come up with leads, which the sales manager would vet first. Ade, the manager, would do an analysis of the clients, and tell the sales staff which ones we should go for. I told him that from now on, the sales staff should be trusted to figure it out for themselves. He seemed a bit dubious, but he was so busy I just about got away with it. Once everyone had got used to the extra responsibilities, we'd start sharing out the tender-writing duties.

Things worked perfectly after that.

For about half a day, anyway.

I was trying to finish a report that was due in the day before, when a harassed-looking Ade stormed into my office. I briefly cursed myself for not having the foresight to install a trapdoor system just inside, and asked him what the problem was.

"The problem," he spluttered, "is your brilliant new idea. More specifically, the sales staff who are carrying out your brilliant new idea."

He said "brilliant" in a pinched, forced kind of way, that suggested he didn't think it was brilliant at all.

"Go on," I sighed.

"Ned has spent all day trying to win over a new client, but the company doesn't have any money, has a history of bad debts, and doesn't have any use for what we're trying to sell them."

"I see."

"He spent over three hundred pounds on a lunch for them, trying to schmooze their business."

"Right."

"If we hadn't been using this fantastic new system, I could have spotted that they weren't suitable straight away. Now we've wasted all this time and money."

He stood there, tapping his foot. He didn't look as if he was going to go away until I'd given him a satisfactory answer. I wondered how much it would cost to install that trapdoor.

"I'll speak to him," I said. "Tell him to come to my office."

He seemed satisfied by this, and flounced out. He was immediately replaced by one of the customer service people, telling me that someone had stolen all the pens from the stationery cupboard.

So much for trust.

I finished typing my report, and printed it out quickly. I had to get over to our southern city branch for a meeting by 4 p.m., and it was after half three now. The unfortunate Ned Harris, who walked in at that point, looked incredibly relieved when I said I had to go out.

"But I'll talk to you first thing in the morning, young man," I warned, sternly.

His eyes fell, and he slunk out of the door.

In the cab on the way back from my meeting (which I had been late for, of course) I wondered what I had done wrong. I'd listened to the mad beach man, that's what I'd done wrong. I bet he was having a good laugh at my expense. You'll never guess what, he'd be saying to his workmates, I met this bloke on holiday, told him all sorts of rubbish, and he believed me! What an idiot!

Yes, very funny. Almost as funny as the traffic jam I was now stuck in. The cab driver leaned on the horn, which failed to make the cars move any faster, but succeeded in making everyone (including me) just that extra bit angrier.

I was furious with the beach stranger. If I ever saw his stupid, grinning face again—

There was a tapping at the window. The beach stranger's stupid, grinning face was grinning at me through the window. He was on a bicycle, wearing some weird green and yellow outfit that made him look like an insect. I wound down the window, about to give him a piece of my mind, but he just looked so damned friendly, I didn't have the heart.

"Hi," he said, cheerfully. "Did you try trusting people, then?"

"Oh yeah, and it's worked out really well," I replied, sarcastically. "My sales manager hates me, we have no stationery left, and I'm even more stressed now than I was before. But thanks for asking."

"Really? What happened?"

And so I told him the whole story, him leaning in the window of my cab, and me sitting inside, sweltering. When I had finished, he smiled.

"Well, I can see what's happened – for a start, I didn't really give you the full picture."

"Oh?"

"Yes, you can't just drop this sort of thing on people and expect them to instantly change the way they work. You need to introduce it, explain what you're trying to do, help them to understand, and provide the training to enable them. Perhaps, I could have been a bit clearer."

"Oh."

"Look, my office is just round the corner – why don't you come in and have a drink, and I'll tell you how to fix it. These cars aren't going anywhere, and your meter is just going up and up."

I thought about it, and agreed to go. The cab driver didn't seem too happy about losing his fare, but I thought he'd probably manage to put the pieces of his life back together somehow.

"By the way," said the beach man, "my name's Charlie."

"Howard," I replied.

We shook hands, and set off towards his office together.

Charlie's office was amazing; I thought we'd walked in the wrong door at first. Lush green plants, huge windows, sofas, smiling faces, and a friendly young man on reception who waved at us as we passed.

We arrived in Charlie's department. More plants, open plan areas, and windows. I saw lots of relaxed, happy, friendly faces. Everything looked relaxed, but somehow not sloppy – there was something in the air, a buzz, a sense of excitement. There were lots of phones ringing, but they were all answered on the second or third ring. The people answering had friendly, relaxed voices, and sounded genuinely eager to help.

I gasped, and pointed, tapping Charlie's elbow.

"Look! That bloke's asleep! Asleep on the sofa!"

"Yes? He's probably tired."

"But... but... he's asleep..."

"Howard, Howard, Howard. He's tired. I don't want him to start messing up what he's working on. I'd much rather he took half an hour to get some rest. You can't work your best if all you're thinking about is getting some sleep."

"Yes, but – he's asleep..."

"Howard, let me ask you a question. Do you judge your people on the number of hours they work, or on the results they get?"

"I don't know. Hours. No, results. Well, there's this guy who always stays till after eight o'clock, he's a really hard worker, and—"

"And how do you know he's a hard worker?"

"Because he stays back so late."

"Maybe he's just not very organised."

"No, he – he stays late. He must be working."

"It doesn't matter what hours people do, as long as they get the results you want. See how many targets this guy meets, and compare it to someone who always leaves at five. I think you'll be surprised."

I shook my head. This was getting difficult already.

Charlie just smiled at me.

"One step at a time, Howard. We'll come back to that one. Don't expect to take it all in at once. Break yourself in gently. Come on, I want you to meet someone."

He took me over to one of the desks, where a cheerful-looking woman sat, writing something on a notepad.

"Howard, I'd like you to meet Catherine. She's very, very good at what she does. Catherine, this is Howard. He's come to see how all our crazy ideas can't possibly work."

I grinned, embarrassed, and shook hands. It turned out that Catherine had started out as an assistant finance person with little or no ambition, but a lot of enthusiasm. She had quickly worked her way up, impressing everyone with her positive attitude and seemingly never-ending supply of great ideas. She absorbed information, new technology, and new ways of working, and was a bit of an inspiration to everyone there.

"So," said Catherine. "You're the beach man?"

I looked at Charlie, who smiled back sheepishly.

"I was telling her about how we met. Did you find your phone, in the end?"

"Oh, right. No, it's gone for ever, I'm afraid. There's probably a lobster somewhere who's making loads of free calls to his brother in the Mediterranean Sea."

They both laughed, with me instead of at me, which made a refreshing change.

"Howard's been trying one of the things I told him about," said Charlie.

"Oh?" said Catherine, interested. "Which one?"

And so Charlie told her the tale I'd told him in the cab. Before he'd even finished, Catherine was nodding and smiling.

"So," she said. "You gave the sales staff the training to be able to judge whether the clients were worth following up, then?"

"Er... no, no we didn't."

Charlie piped up at that point, "Actually, Catherine, that was down to me, I only told Howard part of the story on trusting people – I got it wrong, I'm really sorry Howard."

In my head I couldn't believe what I was hearing – Charlie was telling, no admitting to a colleague that he'd got something wrong – I couldn't wait to see Catherine's reaction to that one.

"I'm sure, Charlie, that you didn't intentionally mislead Howard, weren't you on holiday anyway when you met – I bet you didn't want to get into a long conversation to do with work, however much you wanted to share some of our great ideas, so let's celebrate that one."

Celebrate what? I thought, and that's when I remembered that Charlie had given me his number and asked me to give him a call to hear more – that's funny, why didn't he feel the need to defend himself instead of going straight to an apology to me, how strange these two are.

"Anyway Howard", Catherine continued, "you will need to give your sales staff some training, otherwise they'll just be guessing about what they need to do. Get the sales manager to set up a training day or two, he can tell them what he knows, then, as a team, they can agree principles that everyone can work within. Without information, the staff can't take responsibility. But *with* information, they can't *avoid* taking responsibility."

"You think that'll work?"

> Without information, people cannot take responsibility
>
> *With* information, people cannot *avoid* taking responsibility

"Of course. Listen, we used to have to put our press releases through three levels of checks. Three people had to check and double check them before they went out, so of course it took three times as long to get them finished. The person who wrote the original text didn't feel as if she was trusted to do it properly – sometimes she'd deliberately put in silly things to see if they were spotted. So we decided to let her write them and check them herself, to save time – but she had full training beforehand. She couldn't have known what to look out for, what to check, otherwise; but once she'd had the training, she was able to do it all herself. With the result that when we needed a press release, we could get it out the same day, instead of two weeks later."

"Yes," I countered. "But what if she's off sick? You haven't got anyone to write your press releases." Let's see them talk their way out of that one, I thought triumphantly.

"That happened during the first week we tried it," replied Catherine. "So we trained everyone in the department to write them. It had a great effect on morale, and we could guarantee getting a press release out straight away. Did you see the piece in today's *MoveIt?*"

"It caught my eye," I admitted. I didn't tell them that I'd thrown the magazine across the room, after drawing glasses and moustaches on their faces.

"One of our PAs got that coverage," said Catherine. "She was the first to hear about the contract win, and quickly did the press release first thing that day. That's why we made it into the current issue. Without the information and training, she couldn't have done it."

I didn't say anything. It was a good idea, a great idea, even. If the sales staff knew how to do what the sales manager did, then they wouldn't make the same mistake that Ned Harris had done.

"See if there are any other areas where you could cut out the extra step," said Catherine. "You'll probably find that there are loads of stages you can remove, saving time, money and sanity."

"That's great," I said, sincerely.

"Told you she was good," said Charlie.

"But what about the stationery? We haven't got any pens!"

Catherine laughed.

"Well, buy some more!"

"But they took them all. We can't afford to keep buying them."

"Well, everyone probably needed a pen at the same time, or they just thought they'd grab one before you changed your mind. There isn't much money in selling pens on the black market, so they won't keep disappearing once the novelty has worn off. Give it another go. Trust them."

"Okay, I'll get more pens. But if we go bankrupt because of it, I'll be applying for a job here, I'm warning you now."

They laughed again, and Charlie said he was going to take me to meet some other people. He asked Catherine if she could send him the report once she'd finished it, and she promised to have it ready in half an hour. I waved goodbye to Catherine, and we walked into another area of the building.

"She's very nice," I said to Charlie. "Must be good to have such a great employee."

Charlie looked puzzled.

"Employee? No, Catherine's my boss."

I was shocked. Amazed.

"Your boss?"

"Yup."

"But she just had an ordinary desk, in the middle of all the others."

"True."

"But you just asked her to send you a report when she's finished...?"

"Also true. I need to read the report, so I asked her to send me a copy."

"But..."

"Howard, we don't stand on ceremony here. I needed the report, so I asked for it. She wanted to help me out, so she said she'd try to do it quickly. We're a team here, we all try to help each other as much as we can. Just because she's my boss doesn't mean she has to act like she's more important. We're all important."

I shook my head in disbelief. This was going to take some time, like Charlie said. One step at a time.

🐿 Without information, people cannot take responsibility –
  with information, people cannot *avoid* taking responsibility
🐿 Agree principles that everyone can work within
🐿 Train the staff to do the jobs you're trusting them to do
🐿 Trust them to do it

Chapter 2

Celebrate Mistakes

I was still reeling from the shock of finding out that Catherine was Charlie's boss. Charlie was smiling at me again, which would happen more and more over the next few days, I suspected.

"Right," I said. "As soon as I get back, I'll get the sales manager to sort out that training."

"And what about the sales staff guy?"

"Eh? Which one?"

"The one who spent all the money on the lunch for the client? The client that turned out to be no good?"

"Oh, yes, Ned – well, I'll be seeing him as soon as I get back, too."

"To help him celebrate such a great mistake?" asked Charlie, innocently. I laughed.

"Yeah, that's right. Well done, I'll say, it's coming out of your salary. Do it again, and you're sacked."

"Howard! You can't do that."

He was losing me again.

"Why not?"

"Because he made a mistake."

"Yes, a stupid mistake, and if he does it again—"

"No, no, no – you're thinking about this in the wrong way."

"But mistakes are bad, aren't they?"

Charlie smiled yet again. Told you.

"Howard, when you get back to the office, call Ned into your office straight away. But don't punish him, or tell him off. Celebrate!"

"But he made a mistake!"

Celebrate mistakes

"Yes, but mistakes are a good thing."

This wasn't going well.

"Okay Charlie, I've listened to your ideas, I thought the trust thing was a bit mad at first, but I do see now how it can work. However, this is just too bizarre. Mistakes are bad, full stop. Why shouldn't I punish him?"

Charlie sighed.

"Come on, let's get a drink in the café, and I'll tell you."

The café was almost as big as my entire department. More plants, even bigger windows, bright colours, and more smiling people. I was beginning to think this was some sort of cult. There had to be a catch, they had to be secretly evil, or aliens trying to take over the world or something. This was too good to be true.

I stopped at the coffee and hot water containers, confused.

Charlie handed me a cup, and started to fill his own.

"What's wrong?" he asked.

"Er – where do I put the money?"

"What money?"

"Where's the money slot to pay for the coffee?"

Charlie laughed.

"No, you just take it."

"Oh, right – who do I pay, then?"

"You don't pay anyone. The tea and coffee are free."

"Free? Free tea and coffee?"

"Sure. And fruit juices, herbal teas, biscuits. Oh, not forgetting the ice creams."

Ice creams? Now it was getting weird.

"Free ice creams? But don't people take loads of them?"

"No, maybe the first couple of days new staff members do, but you can only eat so many of them in a day. Most people just have one a day, some people don't bother."

"Free ice creams, I can't see that catching on."

"Let me guess – you have to pay for your coffee?"

"Yes," I grimaced. "Although 'coffee' is a very kind word for it. There's this ancient machine in the basement that spits out a sort of toxic sludge. The machine has got the word 'coffee' written on it, but that's where the resemblance ends."

Charlie laughed again. I laughed with him, just to show him that he wasn't the only one who could laugh.

"Why not buy a cheap kettle and get some coffee and milk for the office?" Charlie suggested. "Even a jar of instant would be better than the machine-made rubbish."

"Now that's the most sensible thing you've said all day," I said.

We took our coffees over to some orange sofas, and sat down.

"Now," said Charlie. "Let's talk about mistakes."

"Off you go," I said, sipping the (excellent) coffee. "This should be good."

"It is. First, let me ask you a question: how do we learn?"

"I don't know, how?"

"Let me say it a different way. Most people in your office use computers, do they?"

"Yes," I replied. "We've all got one now. That's progress for you."

"Okay. Is there anybody in your office who is careful never to make any mistakes when they're using their computer?"

I didn't have to think too hard, before Fred came to mind. "Yes," I said. "Fred never makes a mistake – he's terrified of getting anything wrong."

"Right. And how much new stuff does he learn about using his computer?"

"Well, nothing at all. He knows what he knows, and that's about it."

"Okay, well, can you think of anyone else in the office who does make mistakes on the computer?"

"That's easy – Mina, she's always crashing the machine, losing her settings, sending things to the wrong printer..."

"And how much new stuff does she learn?"

"Learn? Oh, loads, she's always finding new things in the word processor, figuring out new ways of doing things, shortcuts, that sort of thing. People usually go to her when they need help with their machine – I don't know what I'd do without her. I can't manage the damn things at all."

Charlie smiled, and didn't say anything. I saw where he was going with it.

"Yeah, okay, but she still makes lots of mistakes," I pointed out.

"Yes, but while she's doing it, she's learning. You can't learn from your mistakes if you don't make any. The other guy, Fred, he's too scared to try anything different, so while he won't make any mistakes, he won't discover anything new."

"I suppose..."

"People are born enormously intelligent, curious and eager to learn. Think about young children. I saw that you had kids on the beach, how old is your youngest?"

"Hannah? She's three. Three and a half, as she points out."

"I bet she's always asking questions, isn't she?"

"Oh yes – why is the sky blue, where do the birds go when it's cold, where does the rain come from, why do dogs bark and cats meow – she never stops!"

"There you are. She's curious, eager to learn, like all kids. She wants to know about everything, and every time she asks a question, she learns from the answer. And then probably asks fifty more questions. How many sixteen-year-olds are still like that?"

"None at all. Teenagers know everything about everything, or so they like to think."

"Exactly. They don't want to seem stupid, so they make out they know it all, which of course means that it's more difficult to ask questions. What would it be like if your staff were as eager to experiment and make mistakes as a three-year-old?"

"They'd be asking lots of questions."

"Yes! Questions are good. How good would kids be at learning to walk, if every time they fell over, they got blamed and punished?"

"Well, no good at all, I suppose. Good point."

He was right, of course, annoyingly. Mistakes could be a good thing. It would take a bit of getting used to, but I'd give it a go.

On the way out, I stopped and spoke to one of Charlie's staff at random, a guy with an incredibly bright green shirt.

"Excuse me," I said. "I've just been talking with Charlie here about mistakes. Do you really celebrate mistakes here?"

"Oh yes," said the green-shirt man. "My first week here, I accidentally deleted the entire accounts folder on the network."

"I remember that," chuckled Charlie. "That was a good one."

"I was just trying to do my job, and before I knew it, I'd deleted the whole thing. I went and told Charlie straight away. I thought he was going to sack me, but he just laughed and congratulated me on the best mistake of the year."

"Because he'd owned up to it and told me straight away," said Charlie, "we were able to fix it fairly easily. If he'd tried to cover it up, nobody would have noticed until it was too late. He would have got away with it, but we'd have got into terrible trouble with the auditors."

"And I'm pretty much guaranteed not to do it again, now that I've learnt what to look out for," added the green-shirt man.

I left, saying goodbye to Charlie, my head spinning.

I got back to work, and called Ned into my office. He looked terrified, but seemed even more worried when I smiled at him.

"Don't worry," I said. "I'm not going to sack you or anything. I'm just going to congratulate you on your mistake."

He stared at me.

"Look," he said, angrily. "What was the point of getting us all to do something that we don't know how to do? I feel really stupid now; you've just set us all up to fail. You—"

"No, no," I said. "That isn't what I meant. It's good that you did what you did, mistakes are great and we should celebrate them, so well done."

He carried on staring at me, as if a goat had sprouted from my head.

"Well, off you go, then. Carry on."

He left silently, never taking his eyes off me.

Once word got around that it was fine to make mistakes, things started changing slowly. More mistakes were made, sure, but we all had a good laugh about them, and I tried hard not to lay any blame on anyone. But then it started getting worse.

The sales staff had their training from the sales manager, but they still carried on making the same mistakes as Ned Harris had done. The lunches got more extravagant, the clients got less useful, and my hair got thinner.

I phoned up Charlie, in desperation.

"It's all gone wrong," I said. "They're making more mistakes, it's costing us money, and nothing is going right."

"Are they learning from their mistakes?" asked Charlie.

"What?"

"Are they learning from their mistakes, or are they making the same mistake over and over?"

"Er – the same one, usually. Big lunches for clients that don't need our business."

"Howard, think back to the account-deleting story in our office."

"I remember it well, you all celebrated."

"Yep, that's right, and then what happened?"

I thought back to the words of the green-shirt man: "And I'm pretty much guaranteed not to do it again, now that I've learnt what to look out for."

"Oh, he said he'd learnt from his mistake."

Celebrate mistakes...

... and learn from them

"Exactly, Howard. If you don't learn from your mistakes, then the mistakes are not helping your business move forward. What could you do next to help with your situation?"

And then it came to me. "I could explain this to them, and try and figure out a way of making sure that everyone learns from everyone else's mistakes."

"How could you do that, what would work well in your organisation?"

"We could have a weekly mistake meeting, or something."

"Sounds great. How would it work in practice?"

"Erm... we could talk about the mistakes we made, and how we could do it differently next time. That way, everyone would learn from one person's mistake, and there's less chance of it happening again."

"That sounds like it will work really well. Oh, how's the stationery doing?"

"The stationery? Oh, right, it's fine. Just like Catherine said, once the novelty wore off, everyone started being sensible about it, and only took what they needed."

Charlie chuckled.

"Told you she was good."

🐾 Celebrate your mistakes, and learn from them

🐾 Imagine what it would be like to work somewhere where you never got blamed for your mistakes... where mistakes were seen as positive things, as outcomes of risk and innovation

🐾 You can't learn from your mistakes if you don't make any mistakes; go make some

Chapter 3

What to Judge
Your People on

So there we were, with our newly trained sales staff, and our weekly mistake meeting. The mistake meeting, which sounded a bit strange at first, turned out to be a huge success. We all got together and had a good laugh over mistakes, which totally demystified them and took away all the fear. If you made a mistake, it was no longer a shameful, embarrassing event – you got to tell a funny story at the meeting, and we all knew a bit more about what everyone was doing. The sales manager was happy, as he had more time to himself. The staff were happy, because things were slightly different, a bit more loose and relaxed.

I took Charlie's advice again, and bought a cheap jug kettle for the office, a huge jar of instant coffee and a large box of teabags. We then had to buy a fridge to keep the milk in, but we got one of those cool mini-fridges for fifty quid, so it was okay. Before too long, the basement machine was abandoned, and people from other floors started coming in to nick cups of our coffee and tea. This of course meant that the other floors and departments had to have their own kettles and fridges and mugs – but that was fine. The expense wasn't too huge, and the increase in morale was noticeable. I had to admit it – Charlie wasn't completely mad. Although we were a long way from being exactly like his place, we'd started out on the journey.

Things were getting better all the time. A couple of new contracts had come in, which really helped. One even got us a mention in *MoveIt* – although I wrote the press release myself. I wasn't quite ready to hand over everything.

It still wasn't enough, though. The changes were a huge help, but a lot of people were still unhappy, and stressed – and so was I. Something was missing.

Charlie's phone number was now on my speed-dial, top of the list, above even my boss and the CEO. Why not? He was more important, I felt...

"Charlie's not here right now, can I take a message?"

Panic. Where could Charlie be when I needed him?

"Do you know where he is?"

"I think he's in a meeting. Is that Howard?"

It was Catherine. I was saved.

"Yes! Hello Catherine, are you busy?"

"Not too busy to help if I can. What's up?"

I told her about how things were going – better, but not great. She had a quick think.

"How is everyone's morale at the moment?"

"Well, it's a bit low."

"How well are they working?"

"Actually, everyone's working really hard at the moment."

"Hmm. Are you pleased with the actual work they're doing?"

"Yes, of course, they're all doing really, really well."

"Have you told them so?"

"Erm... no..."

"Well, tell them!"

"Tell them?"

"Yes. How are they going to know how much you appreciate them unless you tell them? Recognise when anyone does a good job, and make sure they all know that you're pleased with their work. By showing that you appreciate them, you'll increase their motivation and enthusiasm, and consequently improve their morale."

"That's a great idea, I'll try that now. I'll let you know how it goes..."

I sent an email round, addressed to everyone in the department. We really appreciate everyone's hard work, keep it up, you're all valuable members of the team, and so on and so forth. I sat back, feeling magnanimous, and waited for the love to flow back.

Fifteen minutes later, I had one reply: "Is this a joke?" Immediately after that, the office wag sent me an email with the subject line "To whom it may concern, we heartily endorse your work or contribution, blah blah blah", but no message text.

I was confused and annoyed. What the hell had I done wrong? I'd just told them how great they all were, and all I'd got back was two sarcastic replies. This wasn't working. I phoned Catherine back quickly.

"What do you mean, it didn't work?" she asked. "How did you have time to do it already, we only spoke a moment or so ago?"

I told her about the email, and what I'd said in it. I could almost hear her shaking her head at me over the phone.

"Sorry Howard, you can't just announce that everyone is great, and expect it to work."

"Why not? You told me to."

"I didn't mean this way, sorry, it's too impersonal. How would you feel if someone thanked you for working hard, but didn't mention what you'd worked hard at? Or if someone said how valuable you are, without saying why?"

"Er, a bit patronised, maybe?"

"Exactly, a blanket statement like that just doesn't work well. How will anyone feel that it refers to them? You need the personal touch and you need to be more specific."

"Okay, how do I do that?"

"Talk to them, have a meeting or something. When's your next planned meeting happening?"

"We've got our weekly mistakes meeting tonight."

"Weekly mistakes meeting? Looks like Charlie's having quite an effect on you, then."

"You and Charlie both. It's working, but slowly."

"Then this is exactly what you need. Be supportive, tell them they're doing good work. Better yet, get each person to write down something they appreciate about the person next to them."

I was doubtful about that last one. It sounded a bit lovey-dovey to me.

"I can't imagine my sales manager telling the person next to him how much he appreciates them, and how very handsome he thinks they are. I don't know if they'll go for that."

"It's worth a try, but it will work better if the thing they've appreciated the other person for is something they have done at work. The important thing is to get them to be supportive of each other, to appreciate all the little, usually unnoticed, things that they do for each other every day."

"Well, if you say so."

"I do. Now go and cheer up your people!"

By the time I got off the phone, I'd received another sarcastic email. I closed my email software, and planned for the meeting.

That afternoon, there were lots of expectant faces at the meeting, and I tried not to disappoint them. First, I apologised for the email, and explained that it wasn't meant to come across as so impersonal and insensitive; I asked them to celebrate that one with me. I then told them that I really did appreciate all their hard work, and that they were all doing really well. Then I took a moment to say thank you to each person in the team in turn, for something they had recently achieved.

They softened up a bit at that.

Then I hit them with the next part.

"I want everyone to take a piece of paper. Each piece has one of your names on it – don't take your own, take someone else's. When you get it, I want you to write down one thing you appreciate about that person, and the way they do their work. And it has to be something nice, okay? It's all anonymous, so don't be embarrassed."

"Why are we doing this?" piped up someone in the front row.

"Because we all need to be more supportive of each other," I said. "Including me. I'm going to take one of the sheets as well, and my name is on one of those out there too. Now, the sooner we get on with it, the sooner we can all have an ice cream."

That started a ripple throughout the room. A raspberry ripple, you might say. I casually pointed to the large freezer in the corner of the room. I'd had it brought in at lunchtime, when there weren't many people around. It was full of all kinds of ice creams. It was a bit of an extravagance, but they deserved it for all their hard work. Everyone perked up a bit, and started writing quickly on the sheets of paper.

It worked so well, I decided to make it a regular monthly thing. It really seemed to have an effect on people, seeing nice things written about themselves like that. After a while, people started writing more on the sheets of paper, and morale started to improve. It didn't always work; sometimes people were just too tired to think what to say, sometimes people would have had an argument, and somebody would write something nasty – but it was a start, like all the other things. And the ice creams usually helped, too.

But then Mina came to me, upset. She was the software whiz, very popular in the office, but somebody had written something bad on her sheet of paper, saying that they thought she was lazy and didn't work as hard as everyone else. Mina always left at 5 p.m. on the dot, as she had a family to get home to. Compared to Steve, the guy who always stayed until at least 8 p.m., it didn't look good. I told her not to worry about it, that I'd sort it out.

Of course, I didn't have a clue how to sort it out. I was just stalling for time. Desperately, I called Catherine again. She must have been getting sick of me by now.

"Catherine, I'm stuck. I don't know what to tell Mina. She goes home early every day, but this other guy always stays late – there's resentment, and I don't know how to fix it."

"She goes home early every day?"

"Yes. Well – at five."

"What are her hours?"

"Er... nine till five."

"So she's not actually leaving early. She's just leaving on time, when she's supposed to."

"Yes, technically, but—"

"There's no 'technically' about it. She's not paid to work after five, so why should she stay a second longer?"

"Well—"

"What about the guy who stays late?"

"What about him?"

"What does he do all evening?"

"Gets more work done, I suppose."

"Okay, you need to check something out first, before you do anything. They have targets to meet, things that they need to do, yes?"

"Yes."

"Right. Find out how many of their targets they are meeting. Do it for everyone, not just them. Then you'll see who is doing their work, and who isn't."

"Okay – what do you think that will do?"

"It will give you a solid base to make a decision from. Now go and check, then call me back."

I got off the phone, not looking forward to it. It took a couple of hours, going through the month's reports, figures, accounts, and many other relevant and irrelevant files on the network – but it turned out Catherine was right, as usual. Mina was meeting all her targets, and getting all of her work done. Steve was lagging behind. It made very interesting reading. Excited by this new development, I called Catherine back.

"Sorry," I said. "You must have better things to do than talk to me all day."

"Honestly, it's no trouble. So what's the result?"

I told her about the figures.

"Great work, Howard. So what does it matter what time people leave at, as long as they get their work done?"

"Well, it doesn't, I suppose."

I suddenly remembered something Charlie had said when I'd visited his office that time...

"Charlie once asked me 'Do you judge your people on the number of hours they work, or on the results they get?' This is what he meant, isn't it?"

> "Do you judge your people on the number of hours they work, or on the results they get?"

"Exactly, well done. If people think Mina is lazy because she's leaving when she's supposed to, then something is very wrong there. And this Steve guy is falling behind, so he clearly doesn't have enough time, or needs more support. You need to talk to them both, quickly."

I hurried off the phone again.

It took a while to organise, but I finally managed to meet with Mina and Steve separately, starting with Mina. I showed her the rough report I'd put together, and started the ball rolling. Mina was relieved to see that the figures absolved her of any implied laziness, and then thrilled when I congratulated her on achieving all she had, especially as it was within her working hours. I added that it was great how she had met all her deadlines and delivered everything to such a high standard. Then I let her go, smiling, to get on with her work.

Steve wasn't that surprised when it was his turn to come into the office and see the report. He told me that he'd been falling behind, and was staying late every day to try and make up the work. But somehow the longer he worked, the more time it took him. Thankfully, now we'd discovered this, we were able to do something about it. He would never have come to me about it on his own though, he was just too embarrassed. Eventually, he also admitted that he had written the comment on Mina's sheet of paper – he felt that she had been showing him up. I told him not to worry about it, but that he had to go and tell Mina straight away, and apologise. He promised he would, and got up to leave.

"Just one more thing," I said.

"Yes?"

"Your hours are nine to five. From now on, you will leave at 5 p.m. sharp every day. Nobody works over their hours any more, unless there is a real emergency deadline."

He smiled, and left.

At the next mistakes meeting, I added a new part. Everyone had to say what they were currently working on, just so that everybody could get an idea of what was going on. Seeing the bigger picture, looking at how our targets were fitting into the company principles, just like Catherine had told me. After a few more meetings, we started running out of mistakes, hopefully because we were learning more. At the start of the meeting, instead, I would just ask if anyone had any mistakes to tell us about, and encourage everyone to try more new things, make more mistakes. We would then move on to talking about what we were all up to.

Mina was much happier, and didn't feel guilty about leaving on time any more. Steve started leaving on time too, although he felt strange about it. But he adjusted. We were all adjusting. These were interesting times...

- Judge your people on the results they achieve, not the number of hours they work
- Recognise when people have done good work, give your feedback personally and make it specific
- Look at how your people's targets fit within the company principles and targets – get your people to see the big picture

Chapter 4

Listening is Different from Hearing

He was mad, of course, good old Charlie, but his ideas had been working so far. I had started just accepting whatever he said and going for it. A cruel man could have taken advantage of me, but Charlie only ever wanted to help. I had a weekly lunch with him at this stage, partly to pick his brains for more of those great ideas, but mainly because he was good company. No matter how enjoyable your place of work is, it's always nice to get away from it for a bit and see new people. And we still hadn't got everything quite right yet.

I was just about to leave for the lunch when Yasmin walked in, looking flushed and angry.

"Can I have a quick word, guv?"

"Yeah, sure, it'll have to be quick though, my stomach's got a very important meeting with a café."

"Oh, you should have said it was an emergency you were off to, I'd have called for a police escort."

That wasn't like Yasmin. She was very quiet, hard working, never spoke out of turn. Suddenly I was actually scared of her.

"Something bothering you then, Yasmin?"

"Nice of you to notice."

"Er..."

"It's this deadline I've just been given."

"Right, yes, what about it?"

"It's completely ridiculous. I can't possibly get the whole project done before the end of the month."

"Can't you?"

"No! Of course I can't."

"I see. Well, what if somebody took on your other work?"

"Have you ever lifted your entire house over your head?"

"Eh? Er, no."

"No. Because it's not possible. And neither is this. I just don't have the time, I don't have the information, it can't be done."

"But—"

"Can't be done. Can't can't can't."

"Right. What if somebody helped you with it?"

"Oh, yes, well, if someone helped me, yes of course, I'd have it done in five minutes."

I'd clearly lost control of this conversation some time ago. I tried to remember my Jedi training. What would Charlie do? Work out a way to solve the problem, ask her what she needs.

"Sorry. Erm… Well, what do you need to sort this out?"

"More time, as per usual. This should have been given to me a month ago. And more information. I can't even start it until next week, we won't get the results for the first part until then."

"Yes, of course, good point. What else?"

"This isn't a one-person job. We need one person for each of the four parts. And two months to do it in."

It would be a bit awkward, but she was right – we should have asked for it earlier.

"Okay then, that's what we'll do. Pick out three other people you feel will be able to help out, and I'll change the deadline to two months instead of one."

"Thank you," muttered Yasmin, and walked out without another word. I expected a bit more gratitude, but I suppose she was upset, so I understood. I was quite pleased with myself. Another crisis averted, and I did it all by myself. Well, with the help of Charlie's advice, of course. But I felt good, I felt like I was the hero of the day.

And speaking of Charlie, I was going to be late. I grabbed my notebook (it was always a good idea to have a notebook handy when Charlie was talking, the man was full of ideas, too many to remember) and dashed out of the office.

When I got to the café, Charlie was already there. I apologised for being slightly late, but he shrugged it off with that casual grin of his.

"No problem," he said. "Looks like you're busier than I am – again. Trouble at mill?"

"A little bit," I said. "One of the accounts people just wanted to bite my head off."

"That was nice of them," responded Charlie. "Any particular reason?"

"Basically, she'd been given a deadline which was a bit unrealistic. So

I said, fine, we'll extend it and give you more people to work on it with you."

"Problem solved! Well done you."

"Yes, it's funny though, she didn't seem too happy about it."

"How do you mean?"

"Well, she went ballistic as soon as she got in the door, which is very out of character for Yasmin. And then when I'd sorted it out for her, she still seemed angry. After I'd been so understanding, and all. I felt a bit let down, to be honest."

"So this – Yasmin, did you say?"

"Yes."

"So this Yasmin doesn't normally get so angry?"

"No, she doesn't get angry at all. Very quiet, shy, just gets on with her work."

"Did she say anything else?"

"No, just that stuff about the deadline."

"There must have been something that you didn't pick up on. She wouldn't have got that angry without giving away a clue as to why."

"No, like I said, she was just angry about the deadline."

We ordered our food. I had lost my appetite when Yasmin was shouting at me, but I had got it back now. Once we had ordered, Charlie had a think.

"So," he said. "What, exactly, did she say? Try and remember the precise words she used, if you can."

"Right, er... well, first she said the deadline was ridiculous – completely ridiculous, that was it. She said she couldn't possibly finish it before the end of the month."

"Good, what else?"

"Then... this is very difficult, Charlie, I don't have the best memory in the world."

"It's okay, you're doing great. Just think it through slowly, think about what you said, and her words should follow easily enough."

"I asked her what she needed from me to sort the problem out."

"Very good, you're learning fast. What did she say?"

"More time. She mainly needed more time. What did she say exactly... 'more time, as per usual', that was it."

"Aha!" Charlie raised his finger in the air triumphantly, as if he'd just discovered the Americas. "Did you hear that?"

"What, 'aha'?"

"No! What Yasmin said. Did you hear it?"

"Yes, she wanted more time to do the work."

"Yes, and what else? What was in that phrase that you didn't pick up on?"

"Erm… 'as per usual'?"

"Exactly. What does that tell you?"

"Well, if she says 'as per usual', then that means she always needs more time, because – oh, of course, because she's always getting unrealistic deadlines."

"Well done. That's what you didn't pick up on at the time. And that's why she was so angry to begin with and perhaps why she remained so."

"I've been so stupid, how could I have missed that?"

"You're not stupid, Howard, don't ever think that. You just need to train yourself to listen in a slightly different way. She came in, angry, shouting, and you wanted to know what the problem was. The current problem was the current deadline – but the real problem, the root of her anger, was the fact that she keeps getting these unrealistic deadlines. Once you'd heard about the current deadline, you thought that was the issue making her angry."

"Yes, and I thought I'd sorted it at the time. I just wasn't listening properly."

"You heard her, but you weren't really listening. People say things on many different levels. She was telling you about the current problem, but her anger and some of her words were telling you about the real issue. You need to listen to every word people say, observe their body language, learn to ask relevant questions. If you'd asked her why she was so angry about this one project, she would probably have told you about all the other deadlines. When you get back, ask her if this is a regular issue, and I guarantee you she'll say yes."

> It's not enough to hear,
> you have to really listen

"Okay, I'll ask her. Maybe tomorrow, when she's calmed down."

"No, you should ask her as soon as you get back. Don't let her stew for too long, sort it out quickly and then she'll be happy sooner rather than later."

"Fine – maybe I should phone her now, ask her to come into my office when I get back?"

Charlie shook his head, smiling.

"If you want to terrify her, then yes, do that. If you want to make her feel comfortable, then either don't do it at all, or frame the conversation."

Frame your conversations,
to help people listen better

"Frame it? What, for a crime it didn't commit?"

Charlie laughed.

"Sorry, let me help you understand what I mean. Suppose I was your boss."

"You'd be lucky. Or rather, you probably wouldn't."

"Suppose I was your boss, and I said to you 'come and see me in my office later on', without any explanation. What would you think?"

"Well, I'd be worried. I'd probably think you were going to sack me, or something."

"Exactly. You wouldn't really be going in there with a positive mental attitude. And for the first five or ten minutes of the conversation, you probably wouldn't be hearing anything I said properly, you'd be wondering what was going to happen to you, what you'd done, how you could save yourself from getting into trouble."

"That's true."

"Until you found out what I wanted, you would be all over the place. That's not ideal. But if I said to you 'can we have a chat later on, I want to help you avoid being given these unfair deadlines in the future', what would you think then?"

"Interested, pleased that the issue was going to be sorted out."

"Precisely. And I would have your undivided attention from the moment you walked in. That is what framing a conversation is. You tell the person what the discussion will be about, so they don't spend all day wondering and worrying about what they've done wrong, or how they are going to be punished."

"Right, I see. I'm probably better off not phoning at all then, I'll just ask her to come for that chat when I get back to the office."

"I expect that would be better, yes."

"Charlie," I said, "you've done it again. This lunch will have to be on me today, I feel guilty."

"Why's that?"

"Because I feel like I should be paying you a fortune in consulting fees."

Charlie laughed.

"I'm just trying to spread the message, Howard. The more businesses that think this way, the better for everyone."

The food chose that moment to arrive, which was quite lucky, because I was so hungry I was about to eat my notebook.

When I got back to the office, I called Yasmin in for a chat – and I told her what it was about first, like Charlie said. She spoke first, as soon as she got into the office.

"I'm sorry about this morning," she said. "I just lost my temper, I shouldn't have done it."

"No, you should," I replied. "It's perfectly all right. I would never have noticed otherwise, you're quite right. Now, about these deadlines. I'm guessing that we're never giving you enough time to do the work."

"That's true. It seems to be every single project. I get it too late, I don't have the time, and I never have the information I need until the last minute. It's unreasonable to expect anyone to work like that."

"Yes, it is. So from now on, it's never going to happen again. Any project you're given will be discussed with you first, and we'll arrange a deadline that we can all agree on. You tell us when you can realistically finish the work, and we'll accommodate that. And if, like today, you need more people to work with you on it, then that's what we'll do."

Yasmin sat there and blinked at me.

"Am I being fired or something?" she said, in disbelief. I laughed.

"No, of course not, why would you say that?"

"It's just that – well, it's hard to believe that you're being so helpful. No offence meant, but this is a business, after all."

"I know, Yasmin. But there's no point expecting you to do the impossible, and then shouting at you when you can't do it. It's not like I don't get anything out of it – if you're happy, you'll feel more motivated and be more productive. And hopefully, less inclined to go and work for a competitor."

Yasmin laughed.

"No chance of that now," she said. "I'm too curious to see what happens here next."

She wasn't the only one. I just smiled and brought the conversation to a close. It felt good, it really did. Whatever the reason, I was lucky to have Yasmin. Loyalty was pretty much unheard of in this business.

I owed Charlie more than a lunch. The man was a miracle worker.

🐟 **It's not enough to hear, you have to really listen to people**
🐟 People say more than they actually "say"
🐟 If someone is acting out of character, ask what is really wrong – and how you can help
🐟 Frame conversations, to help people listen better

Chapter 5

Believe the Best

There was trouble in paradise. I knew it couldn't last. I mean, sure, I had hopes that everything would just keep getting better, but deep down the pessimist inside was whispering that he told me so.

I hadn't sacked anyone for a while. I hate sacking people, it's an awful, awful thing to have to do. And no matter how bad it is for me, it must be horrendous for the other person.

But it was looking as if I might have to do it, and fairly soon.

Keith, one of the sales people, was one of our most promising young stars. He'd started at the bottom, worked his way up with plenty of hard graft, and was the top earner nearly every month. He was funny, he was clever, he knew the clients, and he hardly ever came back from a visit without a sale. He was a charmer, could talk all four legs off a donkey, and then convince it to enter the London marathon afterwards – and it would win. That's how good he was. Never missed a day, never late, always eager and ready to break his previous records.

But the past few weeks, he'd started slipping. Just a bit at first, the odd late morning, but then he'd started missing a day here and there, until he was pretty much skipping every other day, or that's what it felt like. He wouldn't explain himself, just mumble "sorry" at everyone when he eventually turned up. He'd clearly lost interest in the job, didn't want to be here, or whatever. He was certainly going the right way about it, if he wanted to get chucked out.

He'd had three warnings. I was going to have to bring him in on a disciplinary. The procedure was a meeting in the conference room with Keith, Ade the sales manager, and anybody Keith wanted to be there just to look out for him, plus me. It wasn't a nice thing to do, but I felt that he'd left me no choice. I couldn't have him just not turning up all the time, not doing the work. It was a bad example to everyone else, people who were putting the work in, and it just wasn't on. Especially after all we'd done for him.

The phone rang. When I answered it, there wasn't much life in my voice.

"Who died?" asked Charlie, cheerfully.

Charlie. I'd completely forgotten, it was Wednesday, our lunch day together.

"Oh, no, I'm so sorry, I forgot all about it – are you there now?"

"Yep – I'm afraid I ordered my sandwich, I couldn't wait. Or rather, my stomach couldn't. Everything all right?"

"No, not really. I think I'm going to have to let someone go."

"Oh dear, that's not good. What happened?"

"Long story. How long have you got?"

"Look, I'm not doing anything urgent this afternoon – why don't you just head down here, get something to eat, and I'll wait for you. You can tell me all about it."

I agreed, and left the office with a heavy heart.

I must have been hungrier than I thought. I put away two sandwiches and a big iced doughnut before I could even get the story out. Charlie watched me stuff my face, amused. When I'd finished, I told him the whole sorry tale.

"Hmm, tricky," he agreed. "So he's just not turning up, coming in late, things like that?"

"Yeah, it's like he's just not interested any more," I said. "He's obviously not happy here, so I may as well do him a favour and cut him loose. Shame, he was one of the best workers we had."

"Hold on now, before you do anything rash. Has he said what's bothering him?"

"No, but he clearly doesn't want to be at work."

"How do you know?"

"Eh?"

"How do you know he doesn't want to be there any more?"

"Well, he – it's obvious, isn't it?"

"Has he said he doesn't want to be there?"

"No, but—"

"Have you asked him what could be wrong?"

"Not as such, no."

"Not as such?"

"Not at all. I just thought he was bored, didn't like the job any more."

"He's been a good worker up to now, Howard, hasn't he?"

"Yes, one of the best, if not the best."

"So what leads you to think the worst of Keith in this situation?"

"Well, that's what happens, isn't it? People just get bored with a job after a while, they want to move on somewhere else."

"If this is the case, why hasn't he?"

"Because – I don't know."

"He was one of your best workers. If he's that good, then he could easily get a job anywhere else, couldn't he?"

"I suppose."

"If he was bored, he would have gone by now. They're crying out for good sales people at the moment, if I didn't like you so much I'd have poached him myself."

"What are you saying?"

"It's very unlikely that his current behaviour is because he is bored with the job. Something else is much more likely to be bothering him."

"What?"

"Good question, go and ask him. You have to believe the best of people, especially your staff. It's all a part of the trust thing. It's best not to just assume the worst of someone based on their current behaviour, especially if it is in complete contrast to before. This guy's a good worker, something must be bothering him. You need to sit down with him, just you and him, and ask him if he's okay."

> Always believe the best of your staff
>
> Believing the best should form the
>
> basis of every communication

"Ask him what he's up to?"

"No, believe the best, remember? Give him the benefit of the doubt. Ask him if he's okay, explain that you've noticed how unhappy he seems, and ask if there's anything you can do to make things better. If you go in there assuming that he's just pulling a fast one, he's going to get even more upset, and really will leave. Believe the best of people, until they give you a reason to believe otherwise. You really don't want to lose him, do you?"

"No, he's a good bloke. We need him. But we need him working well."

"Then find out how you can help. Do whatever it takes. *Whatever it takes*. Remember – believe the best. He's not deliberately trying to mess you about, something is very likely upsetting him. Now go and sort it out, unless you want another sandwich."

I did want another sandwich, but I reckoned it could wait. I was eager to go and talk to Keith.

Keith walked into the conference room looking worried. I tried to reassure him with a friendly smile, but this seemed to have the opposite effect. I made a mental note to practise my friendly smiles in the mirror, so that they wouldn't scare people.

"Come in, come in, sit down, sit down," I said. Say everything twice, say everything twice...

"I know what this is about," said Keith. "When do you want me to go?"

Oh blimey, this wasn't going well.

"No, Keith, I don't want you to go. Look, I can see you're unhappy about something, and I'm worried about you. I just want to know if there's anything I can do to help. You're a damn good worker, and I don't want to lose you."

Keith did a double take. This wasn't what he was expecting.

"Oh. Erm... well, yes, there is something that – well, it's just a bit embarrassing, really."

"You don't have to tell me the details if you don't want to, that's okay. Just tell me what I can do to help."

"No, it's okay, just don't tell anyone else, please."

"I give you my word, it won't leave this room."

"Well, it's... it's my girlfriend."

Now that's exactly what I wasn't expecting.

"Your girlfriend?"

"Yes. She's an IT consultant, so she does a lot of contract work. It's just that the one she's doing at the moment is in New York, and it's not been easy. I just miss her a lot, I mean, she's back in a month, but you know. It's silly, really."

"No, no, that's not silly at all. Don't be silly," I laughed, and was glad to get a tiny smile in return.

"It's the first time we've been apart for such a long time, and what with the time difference, we don't get to speak that much. She wanted me to go and visit, but I've used up all my holiday, and I can't. So I'm just a bit miserable, and I can't really concentrate. I'm really sorry about the lateness and stuff, I'll make it up to you."

"No you won't," I said, firmly. "No need to make anything up to anyone. You're one of our best sales people, we want to keep it that way, so let's not worry about the last month."

"Really?"

"Really. Let's have a think instead about what we can do to sort this out for you."

We chatted for another half hour, and came up with a mutually agreeable solution. He would go to New York to be with his girlfriend for the rest of the time – one month. Because he'd used up his holiday, he'd be "buying" more holiday time – but instead of just not paying him at the end of the month, we'd deduct the money over the next year, to spread it out into smaller, more manageable instalments. I thought it was a fairly good offer, but Keith was delighted with it, more than delighted. He couldn't quite believe that I really meant it, and kept thanking me profusely, which was embarrassing, but felt good all the same. It was great, seeing the change in him, he was like a new man. He left straight away; no point in making him hang around all day when there was a flight to be arranged.

I phoned up Charlie to tell him the good news – and to thank him.

"Thank me for what?" he laughed. "Sounds like you did all the good work."

"Yes, but I couldn't have without your idea. I was going to drag him to a disciplinary hearing!"

"Good job you didn't. This way you get to keep a good worker, and he'll be loyal to you for life."

"True. I'm a bit worried though."

"About what?"

"Well, we're losing our best sales person for a month. I hope the rest of the team can manage."

"They'll be fine. Look at it this way – he's gone for a month, but when he gets back he'll be back to his old self. What would have happened if you had made him stay?"

"He'd have been miserable, not working to his full capacity. He probably would have left us in the end too."

"Exactly. But now you get to keep him, and I bet you a million quid he'll work harder than ever before when he gets back."

"You're a genius, Charlie. Have I told you that?"

"Only once today, but I'll let it pass. I'm not that clever, we had a similar situation here last year. One of our accounts people wasn't doing well in her job, she wasn't happy, and it wasn't looking good for her. Catherine had a chat with her, and found out that she hadn't had the proper training, but was too scared to say anything. We sorted her out with some training, she got more confident with what she was doing, and now she's the second in charge of the accounts department. If we'd just sacked her, we'd have lost a fantastic worker, and we wouldn't even have known it."

"Well, thanks again for helping with the Keith situation, I couldn't have done it without you."

"Don't thank me yet – I still might poach him..."

- 🐾 **Believe the best of people**
- 🐾 Give them the benefit of the doubt
- 🐾 Listen without judgement or assumption
- 🐾 Ask how you can help them

Chapter 6

Hire for Attitude, Train for Skill

"And what would you say your strengths and weaknesses are?"

"Er... I'm really good at, like, fixing things, and stuff like that. Erm... weaknesses... I can be a bit lazy, and I've got this thing where I have to have lots of pens all the time. That's why I left my last job, they sacked me for taking all the pens."

"Hmm. So what is it about TripleX that makes you want to come and work for us?"

"Erm... well, I need the job cos I'm a bit broke at the moment, and I know a bit about computers and stuff like that, so I thought I'd give it a go, like. So what do you do here, anyway?"

"Thank you, that's all we need for now. We'll let you know how you got on."

"Cool – did I get it?"

"We'll let you know."

"Nice one. Cheers mate."

A great philosopher once wrote, "Only mumbling idiots ever come to TripleX for a job interview". Well, maybe that wasn't written by a great philosopher, maybe I just said it myself, but it's still true. A lot of them seemed to have ignored the text of the job advert, and some of them weren't even sure what position they were applying for. Needless to say, they wouldn't be getting a callback.

My eyes glazed over in the third hour, and by mid-afternoon I was rapidly losing the will to live. I only had two more people to see, but was considering just abandoning the whole thing, and telling them to get lost. But they'd come all that way, so I had to at least pay them the courtesy of pretending to listen to them. And we really, really needed that computer support person.

The first one, Nuala, was pretty good. She had all the right qualifications, and really knew her stuff. She was great, actually, and I was quite relieved that at least one of the candidates had what we needed. She was a bit dour and miserable though, but I didn't care, she could do the job. The second one, Harriet, was really nice and funny, but her experience was in other networks, she didn't have a clue about Windows NT, so I really couldn't give her the job. She had a great attitude though, I wished she could have got it instead of Nuala, but there we are.

In other job-related news, I was having trouble with Steve the ex-late stayer again. He was still struggling with what he was doing, and it wasn't looking good. I didn't want to let him go, he was a nice bloke, but I couldn't see any choice. I'm all for being nice and encouraging, and believing the best, but if somebody can't do their job, what else can I do?

When Nuala started, everything was fine for a few days. She didn't get the whole happy smiley thing at all though, and thought we were all completely mad. I told her she should go and visit Charlie's place, that would make us all seem normal. But then it started getting worse. Nuala was never particularly charming or delightful to be around, always sighing whenever you asked her to do something, complaining at how overworked she was, and quite sarcastic whenever anybody didn't know how to do something.

Before too long, everyone was too embarrassed to ask her for any help, with the result that computers kept crashing, work was being lost, and Nuala was getting more and more annoyed with everyone.

I called her in for a quick chat, and explained our principles one more time. It didn't seem to sink in, but as always she pretended to go along with me, and promised that she'd try harder.

This lasted about five minutes, and she was soon making snide comments at people again. She started sending emails round asking people to please not bother her with silly things like the printers not working, she had far too much to do on the network, important things, and if they wouldn't mind at least trying to fix things themselves, that'd be great.

I called her into my office again, and had another quiet word. The atmosphere in the team was becoming unbearable; people would go quiet when she walked past, too afraid to even look at her for fear of getting a sharp remark.

Then one morning she made Mina cry, and that's where I had to draw the line. Mina had been trying to figure out how to do a mail merge using her email address book, and nearly got there as well, but accidentally sent the letter to everyone in the office. Nobody minded, it was just one accidental email, and by the time Mina realised what had happened, she'd figured out how to do it properly.

Nuala came storming into the office, shouted at her, and told her not to be so stupid, messing around with "things she didn't understand". She had a lot of work to do, and Mina was making her life more difficult by "fiddling around" and "playing". Mina burst into tears and ran off, and Nuala huffed and puffed her way back to her lair.

I sent someone after Mina to make sure she was okay, and went chasing after Nuala. I cornered her in her cluttered office, and went ballistic.

She tried to defend herself, but she knew she was in the wrong, and didn't put up much of a fight. I made it clear that we didn't do things like that in this office, and that she needed a serious attitude adjustment if she was ever going to get on with anybody. I felt bad for saying it, but she was a menace, and needed to be told. I don't think I handled it very well, but I didn't really care at the time.

Charlie was away that week – holiday in Dublin with the family, the lucky swine – so he'd asked Catherine to have lunch with me instead. I was sure she'd be sick of me by now, but she was either very nice, or a really good actress.

I sat down heavily in the café chair, as I usually did, with my usual worried frown.

"Charlie told me about this," said Catherine. "The lunchtime frown, he calls it. You need to relax, Howard, don't let things get to you so much."

"How can I?" I said. "It's a difficult time right now. Steve can't do his job properly, and although he tries really hard and is so positive I'm probably going to have to let him go. And then there's Nuala, who is an absolute nightmare and is making everyone miserable. I just don't know what to do. Obviously I can't sack anyone now."

"Why not?"

"Well – we don't do that. Do we?"

"It's up to you, Howard, you're the boss."

"But I thought we had to find out the problem, and help them to sort it out – you know, believe the best, and all that?"

"Ideally, yes. And it does sound like there's hope for Steve, let's come back to him. But every now and again, you'll get someone who just doesn't or can't fit into the way the company works. It sounds like you've been trying to give Nuala a chance, but it doesn't always work out. Occasionally, even though it's never nice, you have to let someone go."

This was news to me. I'd thought Charlie and Catherine were all about peace, love and harmony. But I suppose it made a sort of sense. After all, if somebody just wasn't right for the place, they did have to go. We'd tried everything, but Nuala was just making the atmosphere bad, and affecting everyone's work.

Maybe Catherine could sack her for me. I'd hire her for a day, she could sack Nuala, then we'd all live happily ever after. Well, except for Nuala. Not for the first time that day, I considered buying a farm and raising chickens.

But sacking Nuala wouldn't solve all my problems. I still needed someone to fill her job. And then there was Steve, who couldn't do Nuala's or even his own job properly. It was looking as if today was officially Sacking Day.

"So what do I do now?" I asked Catherine, hoping that her answer would solve all my problems.

"Well, you've got to go back, chat to Nuala, ask her how she feels she is fitting in with the culture, explain it isn't working out from the company's point of view – chances are she will feel the same. You could even temporarily restrict her direct access to staff, while giving her one month to find another job. This way you get technical support for another month, perhaps filtering all requests through an agreeable third party to limit any conflict, and she gets time to look for work. Then you need to get that other person back."

"What other person?"

"The one from the interview, the one with the great attitude."

"Oh, right, Harriet – but she didn't have all the right qualifications. We need her to know NT, and although she knows about other networks she doesn't know anything about this one."

"Howard, at Quad4 we hire for attitude and train for skill."

Hire for attitude, train for skill

"Eh?"

"You said you really liked her, she had a great attitude. So hire her."

"But she doesn't know NT."

"Train her! How long can it take to learn NT if she has comparable knowledge? It's not like she's learning how to be a doctor, it's a software package. Train her up for a couple of weeks, then you've got a knowledge-able, likeable member of staff."

"But – we'd have to pay for a training course, before she can even start doing the job."

"That's not as unusual as you might think. Lots of companies train their employees, send them on courses, even paying for them. I've been on four courses this year, all organised and paid for by my company. The more I learn, the more I can do for the company. It's an investment for them, they want the best employees possible."

"I suppose. Okay, I'll do it, there, see? I can do this."

"Good for you. And what about Steve?"

"Steve? I suppose I'll have to let him go, too."

"Why? Just because he can't do that particular job? What skills does he have that you aren't asking him to use?"

"Well, I've noticed that he's great with the clients when he has to cover the phones for the sales people – but his job is inputting the sales data, not talking to clients."

"Yes, and it's clearly not working out. Maybe he could be trained up as a sales person. Didn't you say things were going well at the moment, and you were thinking of looking for more staff in that team?"

"Yes. I suppose I could ask Steve if he's interested."

"Excellent idea. Put him through the relevant interview tests and see if he has the right skills, first. Set him up to succeed, in a job that exploits his strengths, not his weaknesses. He's a good worker, he's got the right attitude, you don't want to lose him, do you?"

> Set your staff up to succeed
>
> Exploit their strengths,
>
> not their weaknesses

"No, not really. He's a great bloke, he really has got the right attitude."

"There you are then. Ask him what he thinks, and if it works out, look to replace him with a new input clerk."

How come I could never come up with such simple ideas? I telephoned Harriet as soon as I got back, and offered her the job. She was surprised to hear from me, and tried to convince me not to hire her, because she didn't have all the qualifications. I repeated what Catherine had said back to her, almost word for word, but made it sound like I'd just thought of it myself. She was very impressed, and said she was looking forward to working for such a progressive, intelligent company.

"Well," I said, magnanimously, "we try our best."

I'm so cheesy when I want to be. But I meant it, and really wanted to make things work out. I told Nuala the good news – well, not so good for her - but she was fine with it, Catherine was right. She didn't like it here anyway, and was irritated by our "hippy friendly lovey-dovey rubbish", as she called it. I smiled generously, and told her that it wasn't for everyone. I didn't mention that I'd felt exactly the same way as her the first time I heard of it. She loved the idea of having a month to find other work, and Yasmin offered to field all technical requests, so Nuala didn't have to have so much contact with the staff – a win-win situation for everyone.

Steve was next on the list, but that went quite smoothly too. He was unhappy at first, feelling like he'd let his team down. But I made it clear that we wanted to keep him, we loved his attitude and the way he responded to our clients. It turned out that the reason he was so good at the phone cover stuff was because he loved the people contact – something that was lacking in his current job. So we got Ade to train him, and one of the other sales people to buddy him, and wouldn't you know it – he was great at it, a real natural. He picked up everything so quickly because he already knew so much about the company. Of course, he knew the data input side too, so he also worked really well with his old team mates.

We then advertised for a new data input sales clerk – looking for attitude this time, of course – and found that it was much easier when you didn't always have to look out for the exact qualifications. We also introduced one or two team members onto the interview panel. The idea was that they'd have to work with these people, so I wanted to make sure any new staff would get on with everyone else. They even took an active part, asking all the team and attitude type questions, and they really seemed to like being involved in the decision-making process. So all in all, it worked out really well.

So well, in fact, that I started getting worried in case somebody might suggest I'd be better off doing something else. Was I exploiting my strengths...?

- 🐾 Hire for attitude, train for skill
- 🐾 Hire people your existing staff will be happy working with
- 🐾 Skills can be learnt, a good attitude is either there or not there
- 🐾 If somebody is not happy in their current job, see if they can do something else better
- 🐾 Set your staff up to succeed – exploit their strengths not their weaknesses

Chapter 7

Taking Full Responsibility for Your Own Life

Harriet, the new support person, was working out really well. She was still in the middle of her training period, but she was a fast learner, and everybody thought she was great. It was such a relief to have removed the big hole of negativity that Nuala had brought in, and make things cheerful again. Steve was happy too, in his new role, and left every day at 5 p.m., like he was supposed to.

But of course, if I've learned anything about the world of work, I've learned that things are never perfect for very long.

Somehow, Clive, my area manager, heard about what had happened with Harriet and Nuala. He wasn't at all convinced that this new approach of mine (well, of Charlie and Catherine's) was a good idea, and was very keen for me to fall flat on my face.

I was working on an urgent report in my office when Clive burst in, all red-faced, huffing and puffing indignantly.

"What's going on?" he demanded, fixing his beady eyes on me.

"Where?" I asked. He was bigger than me, but I wasn't going to let myself be intimidated. Clive had been my area boss for a couple of years, and wasn't exactly responsive to change. To a certain extent, I was left to get on with running things the way I wanted, but he saw everything that went on. He'd made it clear informally that he wasn't in favour of all the new ways of working that I had introduced, and thought that they would cause trouble in the long run. He was itching for some proof, some big mistake that would prove once and for all that I was deluded, and dragging the company into the poorhouse.

"You know what I mean," he said. "All this namby-pamby stuff has gone too far. You got rid of a perfectly good worker, and hired some idiot who doesn't even have the right qualifications. What possible reasons do you have for this?"

I thought very carefully about what to say.

"Nuala was creating a bad atmosphere and affecting people's work," I said. "Harriet gets on with everyone, and we've nearly finished teaching her the stuff she needs to know. I don't see that there's a problem."

"Oh, you don't see that there's a problem? Right, well, I guess there isn't one, then. What are you trying to do, Howard? Have you gone mad?"

He was starting to annoy me now.

"Yes Clive, I've gone mad. I'm mad, just because I don't agree with you about something. Clearly I'm insane, I mean, no right-thinking person could ever possibly disagree with you, could they?"

"That's not what I'm saying."

"Yes it is, it's exactly what you're saying. You're right, I'm wrong, the end. Well I'm sorry, but it doesn't work like that."

"Doesn't it? Fine. Get rid of Harriet, and get Nuala back. End of story."

"Can't be done, I'm afraid. Nuala wouldn't want to come back, and I wouldn't take her even if she did. Harriet's doing really well, and I'm not messing everything up now."

"I take it back – you are mad. And stupid."

"This conversation is over, Clive. Please go away."

He stormed out. I breathed a sigh of relief.

But these things never go away. Now that we'd officially declared our animosity, we had to avoid each other, ignore each other if we met in the hallways, and talk about each other behind our backs. It was all very unpleasant. And confusing – I'm sure that I ended up talking about myself behind my own back, once.

One day I came out of my office to grab a quick coffee, only to see Clive hovering around the coffee area. He was chatting with someone else, but I couldn't go over there to get my coffee, or there would be an awkward silence, wouldn't there? So I waited in my office until he went away. He didn't go for ages though, but if I left, he would see me, and I didn't want another confrontation. This was ridiculous, I was hiding in my office! What was I, twelve years old?

Apparently, yes, I was. After a while, I felt a pressing urge to go to the toilet. Too much coffee already that day. And still Clive remained rooted to the spot, like a tree in a cheap suit (and atrocious aftershave). What could he possibly be talking about? Didn't he have any work to do? What kind of an area manager would hang around the coffee machine for hours – okay, fifteen minutes – gossiping? Clive's kind, obviously.

Eventually, I just had to grit my teeth and walk past him. He completely ignored me, which was incredibly annoying, because I'd just been hiding in my office for ages for no reason. I could have left at any time! I bet he did it on purpose...

I phoned up Charlie and Catherine's place, hoping for a quick fix, an easy answer. But life is never that simple, so I knew they were going to tell me to do something I didn't want to do. Catherine came on the line, and did exactly that.

"Howard, you're going to have to talk to him."

I knew it.

"But I don't want to, why can't I just fix it without involving him?"

"How can you fix a situation involving two people with only one of them?"

"Er – easily and quickly?"

"No. You need to talk to him."

"But he's the one who's in the wrong – why can't he come and apologise to me?"

"Two reasons: first, while you think you're in the right, he thinks he's in the right. Second, what does it matter who makes the first move?"

"It's the principle of the thing."

"Principle's all well and good, but if the situation isn't getting resolved, you need to do something. It's your job, Howard, and your life. Take full responsibility for it, make the first move. It doesn't matter who does, as long as it gets sorted out."

> Take full responsibility for your life

"I suppose."

"Trust me Howard. I'm a doctor."

"No you're not."

"Okay, maybe not, but trust me anyway..."

So I did. She'd never steered me wrong so far, and neither had Charlie. I had nothing to lose but my self-respect.

I went to Clive's office, and politely knocked on the door. He beckoned me in.

"What is it?" he said.

"Look," I said. "I'm sorry about that argument we had, it got out of hand, and I just wanted to come and explain my position to you properly, now that we've both calmed down a bit."

He looked surprised, as if he'd been expecting an argument.

"Okay, go on," he said.

"Well, here's the thing: Nuala knew her stuff, but she was an absolute nightmare. She couldn't get on with anyone, so she wasn't actually doing her job properly. Nobody would call her when their PC broke, so we lost hours of work."

"You should have told the staff to get over it, deal with it."

"I did. I also told Nuala to be nice, but she just got worse. So we brought Harriet back. Everyone gets on with her, and now that she's finished her training, she knows the job just as well as Nuala did. The difference is, people can work with Harriet. They couldn't work with Nuala."

"Yes, that's great," said Clive. "But this is a business. Not everyone is going to get on, you can't just hire nice people."

"Why not? Why can't we make it a nicer atmosphere? It doesn't help anyone if there's bad feeling like that. Yes, it is a business – and it makes good business sense to keep everyone as happy as possible."

"Hmm. I suppose. Maybe. You have to admit though, it's a bit weird."

"Oh yes, completely – I had my doubts myself, but it's working out really well."

"Well... okay, let's see how Harriet does then. I'm sorry Howard, I should have trusted your judgement more."

"Thanks, Clive. I really appreciate that."

I think I won. Or maybe he did.

"You both won," said Catherine, when I phoned her later on.

"Eh? How did we both win?"

"You ended this silly argument, you can now walk the halls without fear, you got Harriet to stay, and Clive isn't angry any more. You both got good things out of it. See? It didn't matter who made the first move. You both took positive steps, and sorted it out together."

"Yes, I suppose we did."

"It's all about creating the world you live in. For example, I used to be terrified of dogs. Whenever I went to the park, dogs would chase me, bark at me, and generally scare me. My friends assured me that dogs were actually lovely, friendly animals, but I wasn't having any of it. One day, I'd had enough. I attended a workshop which helped me to realise that I was responsible for creating the world I lived in – I decided that I wouldn't let dogs scare me any more. After that, my world changed. Dogs stopped chasing me and barking at me, and I relaxed more."

"I prefer cats, personally. But how can the way you feel affect other people? Or animals?"

"Well, suppose you went to a party, but were convinced that everyone there didn't like you, didn't want to talk to you. How would you behave?"

"I'd be really quiet, not make eye contact, keep out of the way."

"How do you think people would react to that?"

"Er... they'd probably avoid me, too."

"Exactly. If you went there desperate for company, people would see that too, and pull away. But if you went along feeling relaxed and confident, then people would want to talk to you, thinking that you're interesting and fun to be around. You create the world you live in – so why create a world that is anything less than the best?"

"I see what you mean. Fair enough. We both won, then."

"That's more like it."

"But I won, really."

"Howard..."

🐾 Take full responsibility – it's your life

🐾 Create the world that you live in

Chapter 8

Job Ownership and Full Involvement from Everyone

Our landlord was a jolly man. He smiled a lot, laughed a lot, and you never saw him frowning. That's probably because he got to sit by his swimming pool all day while we paid him loads of money to rent out the fairly cramped premises in the centre of the city. To be fair though, he'd been quite a reasonable chap. The odd rent increase here and there was only to be expected. The big bosses didn't like dealing with people, so I had been landed with the job of liaising with him, but he was never too unreasonable.

This time, however, he had gone too far.

"You're selling?" I repeated, for the fifth time. I heard him chuckling on the other end of the phone, probably sitting by his pool.

"Howard, what can I say? They made me an offer I couldn't refuse."

"Of course you could refuse — just say no."

"Okay, let me rephrase that: they made me an offer I didn't want to refuse."

"That's more like it. Can I ask how much?"

"You can."

"How much?"

"None of your business."

"Fair enough. What are we supposed to do then? You're turfing us out on the street, you know."

"Relax, relax — it's not as if it's happening tomorrow. You've got another eight months left in your lease, plenty of time to find other premises."

"But we like the ones we're in."

"I know, they're very nice. But I'm selling. I want to get out of this business, this way I get to retire ten years early. Have myself a nice rest."

"Yes, you must be exhausted taking all of our rent money to the bank. I don't know how you cope, I really don't."

"Don't be like that, Howard, it's nothing personal. You didn't expect to rent the place for ever, did you?"

"No, but I thought—"

"I'm very sorry, but there's nothing either of us can do. I've signed the papers, the deal is done. I've given you enough notice, you'll find somewhere else in time."

"But where will we go? What will we do? What is to become of us?"

He chuckled.

"Relax, Howard, you'll be fine. After all, tomorrow is another day."

After I'd hung up, I wished I'd slammed the phone down to make myself feel better. So I picked it up again, and slammed it down. I felt a little bit better, but it just wasn't the same. I briefly considered asking somebody to phone me up so that I could slam the phone down on them, but I didn't think anyone would be interested in helping me out.

Moving. We have to move. Simple enough for a person, but this was a whole business we were talking about. People, equipment, networks, desks, phones – we'd have to change the letterheads, phone numbers, tell all our clients – it was a nightmare. And before any of that could happen, I'd have to break the news to everyone in the building. That would be even worse. We'd have to start looking for places, and then when we found one, none of the staff would like it, and they'd all complain, and it just wouldn't be pretty at all.

I made a mental note never to be nice to a landlord ever again.

Opening my notebook to a fresh page, I made a list of options.

Options

1) Gazump buyers and buy building ourselves. Advantages: we'd own the building and stay here, and I like the word "gazumping". Disadvantages: we'd be bankrupt, because we can't afford it.

2) Move to other location. Advantages: none. Disadvantages: staff unhappy, moving is difficult, expensive, time-consuming. I may also go insane.

3) Refuse to leave building, become squatters. Advantages: don't have to pay rent, stay in building. Disadvantages: no electricity or water, staff have to go to toilet in a bucket.

4) Lock myself in office, put pants on head, start a small fire in the middle of the room, and dance around screeching "jabber-jabber-jabber". Advantages: good for a laugh, helps me avoid the issue. Disadvantages: they'll take me away for my own good.

I carefully removed the page, folded it up, and ate it. This wasn't helping. I looked up, and saw that Yasmin had walked into the room. She was standing there, gaping at me. I straightened up, and tried to appear as if making notes and eating them was perfectly normal behaviour for a man of my importance, and that once she had reached a similar position on the corporate ladder, she would understand this.

"Yes?" I said, my voice wobbling only slightly.

"Someone to see you," she said, leaving the room quickly. If she'd been going any faster, she'd have been sprinting. I tried picking up the phone and slamming it down again, but the magic was gone.

Charlie bounded into the room, like a big labrador in jeans and a T-shirt.

"Howard!" he said. "Thought I'd pop in and say hello. How's it going?"

"Wonderful. I'm eating paper, and Yasmin thinks I'm mad. Oh, and we're about to be thrown out of the building."

"Thrown out? How come?"

"Our lease is up in eight months, and the greedy landlord is selling the place. Probably going to turn it into one of those pubs where they only sell bottles, everything costs a fortune, and the music slowly gets louder as the evening goes on."

"Er… okay. So you have to move, then?"

"I guess so, yes."

"Oh. Well, never mind, this place was a bit too small for you anyway, wasn't it?"

"Was it?"

"Yes, you're always telling me it is. It's too small, we need a bigger place, and so on."

"Yes, I suppose I have been. I just didn't think we'd ever bother, you know? It's so awkward moving anywhere."

"Well this could be just the opportunity you're looking for."

"Yes, but wherever we go, the staff aren't going to like it."

"Why not?"

"They're used to this place. The other place is going to be too far away, too close, too big, too small, too purple, too whatever."

"Have you spoken to them yet?"

"No, I don't know what to tell them."

"Tell them the truth. You have to move, the landlord is selling, so you need to find another place."

"Oh, I hadn't thought of that. Yes, I'm sure they'll feel much better once I say it like that."

"Howard, don't be so negative all the time! Honestly, you're like a big negativity panda, or something."

"Panda?"

"If it's something everyone has a hand in, then they won't feel so bad about it."

"A panda, Charlie?"

"Never mind the panda. Look: job ownership is a big part of Quad4. We all pretty much define our own jobs, and we all have a say in most of the things the company does."

"What do you mean, you define your own jobs?"

"Exactly that. Everyone decides what jobs they want to do, and how to do them. If they get bored, they can change jobs."

"That sounds like a recipe for disaster."

"It's fine, honestly. But let's concentrate on this problem first."

"Okay. What can I do?"

"Why do you need to do anything?"

"Well, I'm the boss. And I'm in charge of the whole landlord and building thing, so it's down to me."

"Let me ask you something: what do you see as the key role of a manager? A manager of people?"

"Erm... to be decisive, good at strategic thinking, good communicator?"

"Okay, here's another question: when have you worked at your absolute best?"

"How do you mean?"

"When did you really rise to a challenge, achieve something you were proud of?"

"Well, there was that big project last year – it was a last-minute thing, and the manager who normally dealt with that particular department was off sick. My boss asked me if I could do it, nobody else had a clue, so I gave it a go. It wasn't perfect, but I was really pleased with how I coped with it."

"So you work best when you're challenged, and trusted to do things your own way?"

"I suppose so, yes."

"So let's assume this is true of most people. In that case, what should the key role of a manager be?"

"Erm... trust people? Keep out of the way, let them get on with it?"

"Exactly. Before I worked at Quad4, I ran my own training company. When I started, I was very full of myself, and thought that my biggest difficulty was finding trainers as good as me. So when I got new trainers, I would sit in on their training sessions and give them detailed notes of what they did right and wrong. How do you think they felt about that?"

"They probably wanted to make you eat the detailed notes."

"And worse. I realised that I was trying to make everybody train in exactly the same way as I did. Trouble is, nobody can do that, nobody wants to. On the other hand, I couldn't just have every trainer doing completely different things. So I got together with them and we agreed the core principles that they could work within. Things like asking instead of telling. We used an age-old statement of principles: 'Tell me and I will forget; Show me and I may remember; Involve me and I will understand'. Then we agreed targets, based on leaving clients feeling happy, confident and capable, and measured these by having evaluations at the end of the day. So if your people are working within agreed principles and achieving agreed targets, why do you need to worry about what they're doing?"

"I don't, I suppose."

"Good. There are other elements of this, like feedback. Where do most people get feedback from, at work?"

"Their managers?"

"Right. But where should they get it from?"

"Customers?"

"Precisely. Getting appraisals once a year is no good. It would be like playing a game of football, and not finding out if you won for a year, or even if you scored a goal or not. Even then, they wouldn't know if they'd won, only if the manager thought they'd won."

"It wouldn't be a very exciting game."

"True. The crucial part, though, is support."

"Ah," I said. Now I thought I understood. "You mean management?"

"No," replied Charlie. It looked like I hadn't understood. "I mean support. We don't call our people managers, we call them coaches. The difference is that the member of staff decides if and when they want to see the coach. They get support, and the chance to work through things. It gives people the freedom to experiment and innovate. After a year, all the other trainers were much better than I was. Some of them were winning awards for being the best trainers in the country."

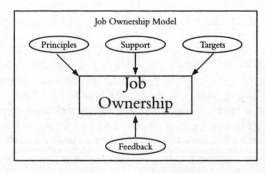

54

"Yes, that's all very well in a training company, Charlie, but how can that help me with this office move?"

"Just adapt it slightly, as it's a different situation. What is the target?"

"To find a new office."

"Okay, well see if the staff can work out a way of doing it smoothly. What benefits could a team of people working on this bring to the situation?"

"Perhaps they could sort out some places we might want to move to, feed it back to everyone, then we can all see what we think."

"Great, what else would help the staff to feel that they were a part of the decision-making process?"

"We could take our people round to each site, see what they think. If everyone has a say, then they'll feel better about the final decision."

"Well done. People like to think that their opinion matters in their job. It makes them feel valued, important."

"You really think that'll work?"

"Of course it will. It's their company too, so they should get a say on where you go anyway. It's a lot better than just stressing yourself out doing it all by yourself, and then just telling them where they're moving to, without giving them a choice. And it can't hurt."

"Yes, I suppose you're right."

"Course I'm right, Howard. Have I ever steered you wrong?"

"Well, no," I admitted. "Not yet, anyway."

"That's the spirit!" enthused Charlie. "Well, I'd better get on, just popped in to say hello really. Good luck with it all."

He bounded out again. Papers fluttered in his wake. Whenever I spoke to Charlie, I always felt like I'd been on a five-mile run, or jumped into a cold bath. In a nice way, of course.

The next week, I tried what Charlie had suggested. I set up a team to research new premises, and told everyone what was going on. They took it much better than I had expected, and seemed quite excited at the prospect of picking a place to move to. We narrowed it down to four sites, and then there was the problem of getting everyone there. After some creative thought, we hired a load of minibuses, closed at lunchtime one Friday, and drove everyone to each site separately. It was a great laugh, like a school trip or something. The first site was no good, the next two were quite good, but the last one was great. It needed a bit of work, but the good thing was, we could design the interior layout ourselves. That meant that we'd be able to decide what went where, where there would be walls, desks, toilets, etc.

On Monday morning, we took a vote, but there was probably no need.

When the fourth site emerged as the unanimous winner, it was no surprise to anyone. The staff were delighted, and really looking forward to moving. The interesting thing was, it meant a slightly longer journey for most of them. The other three sites were much nearer. But they wanted this new place, so it was fine.

I could hardly believe it. A catastrophe had been turned into a birthday present.

Another interesting side effect of the whole involvement and ownership thing was what happened with the finances. It always took ages to sort out the salaries every month, for various reasons that I won't even pretend to understand, with the result that they were regularly a few days late. Most people were okay about it, but it was awkward when you had direct debits going out on the day your salary was supposed to be in your bank account.

Anyway, a couple of finance people came to me one day with some sheets of paper, saying they had an idea to streamline the salary process and save lots of time. Would I read it, make sure it was okay, and put it into action? Normally I'd have had to scrutinise the whole thing, worried that they were doing it wrong or trying to put one over on me. This time, however, I didn't even look at the papers.

"Tell you what," I said, casually, "work out the fine details yourself, give it a go, and see what happens. You know the systems better than I do, so if you think it's worth a try, then go for it. You're in charge of the finances, so you decide if this goes ahead or not. Let me know if it works."

They left, almost as surprised as if they'd found me eating notepaper – what a thought! But they were excited, eager to see how they could manage it. I felt great.

I phoned up Charlie to thank him.

"No need to thank me, Howard, it was all down to you and your team."

"Yes, but I would never have come up with the idea by myself."

"You would, I have faith in you. You kept an open mind, you carried it through, and it got done. Everybody's happy, and that's the important thing. Most companies have specific ways of doing things, which stops anyone trying new things. It stifles innovation, and nothing ever gets improved."

Yasmin popped her head round the door. I covered the mouthpiece, and waved her in.

"Sandwich man's here, guv," she said. "You want the usual? Or will you be okay with your notebook?"

"Usual, please," I said, throwing a crumpled-up ball of paper at her. "And kindly sack yourself while you're at it."

She disappeared with a grin, deftly avoiding the paper.

"Yes," I said to Charlie, "but you can't avoid the credit that easily. You really helped out, and I appreciate it."

"No worries. Just remember the job ownership idea for the future. Keep them all involved in big decisions like this one. You'll be surprised again, I guarantee it."

"I'm sure I will, nothing is ever predictable where you're involved, I'm rapidly learning that."

"We aim to please."

"Right, I'd better go, I've got a sandwich coming."

"Sure thing. Enjoy it – and good luck with the move, when it happens."

"Cheers, I'll see you later. Oh, and Charlie?"

"Yes?"

"Would you mind terribly if I slammed the phone down on you? Only I'm still a bit stressed out today, and I need to vent a bit."

He laughed.

"If it makes you feel better, go right ahead."

"Thanks Charlie, you're a star," I said warmly. Then I slammed the phone down on him. It felt great.

- Create a framework which gives people ownership over their jobs
- Get everyone involved in the decisions that affect them
- If people are involved in decision, they will be more committed to making those decisions work

Chapter 9

Work/Life Balance

And so, eventually, the Big Move finally happened. They say moving house is more stressful than divorce or bereavement - I think moving a business is more stressful than a world war. It took a while. A very long while. But everyone pulled together, put in their fair share of work, and it all went a lot more smoothly than it would have in the bad old days.

We actually threw away a lot of unnecessary stuff, too, that would have just been cluttering up the new offices. When you move house, you always find that you've accumulated loads of rubbish; when you move a business, multiply that by a hundred, and you'll be on the right track. There was one small room in particular that was like an optical illusion – just when I thought we had got the last box of files out of it, we'd find five more. It was never-ending, as if there was a magic machine in there that was creating boxes of paper out of thin air. Endless lines of boxes, piling up in the corridor for us to sort through. I was convinced that if we tried to put them back, we wouldn't be able to fit even half of them back in that little room. I didn't want to test this theory though.

We'd made an announcement to all our clients and contacts that we would be shutting things down for a few days to sort the move out, and they were fine with it. Everybody turned up in old clothing, and we managed to get most of the stuff moved in a day, which was amazing. We got a removal company to take the bulk of it, so when we arrived at the new offices, everything was there, ready to be unpacked.

The new building was great. The refurbishment had only been finished the week before, so it all smelled clean and fresh. Everybody had more room to move. The last place had been too cramped, too ugly and rather unpleasant. The new place had bigger windows, more space, more air and more light. I'd copied lots of ideas from Charlie's place, so we had plenty of plants and bright colours. Funnily enough, I didn't think he'd mind.

Things were really good. Half of the time, it didn't even feel as if it was a job, instead it felt as if I was helping out a bunch of mates with some fun projects. That sounds a bit corny, but it was true, it really was. I was relaxed and happy, and so was everyone else. Most offices have a tense air of competition; you daren't admit not knowing anything, for fear of looking stupid. People are afraid to ask questions for the same reason. With the result that they end up doing things wrong all the time, which causes more trouble for everybody. But we were doing great, nobody felt the need to act superior; we all tried our best to help each other out. It was much healthier.

But inevitably, something had to happen to stress me out, and it came in the form of a delegation from the finance department.

They didn't want extra money, or time off, or a new toy – they wanted flexible hours. As if we were the sort of company that could just let people turn up when they felt like it, and go home early. Things needed to be done at certain times, phones needed to be answered, clients needed to be contacted, the business had to be run. Flexible hours would mess everything up. It was the one thing I couldn't give them.

I decided to drop in on Charlie unannounced. I was still convinced that there was a catch to all his lovey-dovey stuff, and that if I went there without warning I'd find them all doing terrible things, or hatching evil plans to enslave the human race, steal our water, and take us back to their planet for food. I think I almost felt disappointed when I arrived and found the same happy, friendly place.

Charlie wasn't around that day (probably back on the mothership, plotting some nefarious scheme involving probes), so I had the pleasure of Catherine's company again. She was quite busy, but she happily gave me some time to chat. She could tell that I was troubled.

"Are they working you too hard again?" she asked.

"No, not really, it's quite relaxed at my place now," I replied. "Not up to your standards yet, of course, but we're getting there, slowly."

"That's good to hear. So what's causing that frown?"

"Oh, a few people from finance. You know we've just moved across town?"

"Yes, Charlie was telling me about it. Very creative solution, letting the staff pick the place you move to."

"Well, I can't take all the credit for that, Charlie helped me come up with the idea."

"Maybe, but you went for it, and carried it out."

"I know. Maybe I've given them all a bit too much leeway."

"What do you mean?"

"They're starting to ask for stuff now."

"Ooh, shocking! What kind of stuff? Diamond-encrusted office chairs?"

"No, nothing like that. But I think now things are more relaxed, they're taking advantage a bit. They all want flexible hours."

"So?"

"They just want to come in when they feel like it, and do different hours."

"What's the problem?"

"Well, we don't do things like that."

"Why do you think it's a problem, though?"

"Because they'll take advantage."

"Do you trust them?"

"Yes, but – oh, right."

"If you work through the problem, you'll see that there isn't one."

"How do you mean?"

"They want flexible working hours – so let them have them."

"Yes, but they'll just come in at all hours, and leave early."

"No, that's not what flexible hours are. Could be that you're still hung up on your old mindset, looking for the catch, wondering how they're going to take advantage. How are your people different now?"

"They're working much harder, feeling more motivated and enthusiastic."

"So why would they suddenly try to take advantage now?"

"Don't know. Because they can?"

"No. That's exactly why they won't. They're trusted, so they won't betray that trust. If some people want flexible hours, they must have a good reason for it. Why not have a chat with some of them, see what the situation is? Not everybody wants it, do they?"

"I don't think so, no."

"Well there you go, then. As long as people meet their targets, and do the agreed number of hours a week, what does it matter when they arrive or leave?"

"It doesn't, I suppose. But we need people in at nine to answer the phones."

"Does everybody have to be in to answer the phones?"

"No, I suppose not."

"Then have a rota, get them to take turns. People who can make it in early can do the morning shift, people who come in later can do the afternoon one. And if you have people staying until the evening, then you increase the hours during which you can take calls, which is better for the customers. Get the staff to work it out themselves, they'll probably come up with a better system if it's in their interest to do so."

"I don't know, Catherine. It sounds a bit risky. I don't want to mess everything up."

"Give it a try. If it really doesn't work, you can always go back to the old way. Just try."

So I did. We all did. I told everyone that if they wanted the flexible hours, they needed to sort out some sort of rota, as Catherine had suggested. As long as the phones were covered during all the working hours, I told them, then it wasn't a problem.

They all went off into a huddle for an hour. There was much talking, much scratching of heads, much scribbling on flipcharts with big pens.

Eventually they came back with a crooked grid drawn on the paper. They'd worked out a rota system. The people who could make it in earlier would cover the phones in the morning, but could leave early. The people who needed to come in later, or who had travelling difficulties, would cover the phones and stay later. It was very clever.

It got even cleverer than that, though, and more complex. Mina wanted to spend one day a week helping out at her kids' school, so she spread her hours over the other four days. I hadn't even thought about something like that. Then of course, the floodgates opened; not in a bad way, it was just that nobody had ever tried to help the staff out like this before. They must have all been unhappy with the hours up to now. Two people wanted to work term times and stay away during school holidays, so they could be with their kids as often as possible. Some people liked taking lots of holidays in the sun, some people just didn't like getting up early. It transformed the place almost overnight. People who had been tired, lethargic, or unenthusiastic were now well-rested, bright-eyed, bushy-tailed, and eager to take anything their jobs could throw at them.

Even I benefited from this – or rather, Helen and my kids did. I was coming home on time, and able to help my kids out with their homework. Well, the homework that I could manage – some of the maths gave me a bit of trouble, but luckily they were better at it than me. Gone were the days when I would be locked in the spare room, going over reports, working on things that needed finishing urgently. When I got home, I completely forgot about work. Helen wondered what had happened to me. She thought I'd been replaced with a pod person or something, but she wasn't complaining, so she wasn't bothered about a potential alien invasion, as long as our home life carried on the way it was going.

And when one of our people, Tom, wasn't doing his hours, we didn't notice it from his comings and goings – we noticed because he wasn't meeting his targets. The quality of the work was what mattered. Making sure to believe the best, I called him in to see if he was okay. It turned out that he hadn't noticed he wasn't doing his hours, he was just so relaxed about coming in and out, his hours had just been slipping away. He was very embarrassed, but I told him not to worry. He promised to make up the time from now on, and I believed him. So overall, the whole flexitime thing was working out really well.

I was congratulating myself on my clever idea (well, Catherine's, and the staff's) when Mina came to see me. She thanked me for the flexible hours, and admitted that she'd been thinking of leaving the company until now. She'd wanted to spend more time with her children, and this had helped her to do this. So she was very happy indeed, and so was everyone else. I couldn't believe it had actually worked – and that everyone was working even harder as a result. But it was true.

- 🏹 **Help people to balance their home lives with their working lives**
- 🏹 If people are happier with the balance of their lives, they will be more motivated and produce better work

Chapter 10

Putting It All Together

I suppose it's true what they say – pride really does come before a fall. I was so pleased with myself, so proud of what the company had become. The staff were happy, the clients were happy. Everyone was working harder than ever before, but not, crucially, because things were more difficult; it was because everyone enjoyed what they were doing so much. It sounds really cheesy to say this sort of thing, but it was true. We were really happy. We were all pulling together. Nobody was stressed, the place was bright and cheerful, and nothing could possibly go wrong.

But of course, when you say things like "nothing could possibly go wrong", that's exactly when things do.

Nobody was really sure how it happened. It was a combination of things, really. The market was taking a sharp downturn all over the country, so we weren't the only ones suffering. The housing market had gone a bit crazy too, so people needed more money for themselves. Businesses were being that much more careful about spending money, scrutinising every decision minutely. Clients took longer to pay, and some didn't – couldn't – pay at all. We had an excellent credit chaser, but she could only do so much. If the clients didn't have the money to pay us, then nothing she did could make them. The service charge for the building had just gone up too, which was hurting us a lot. To top things off, everyone was due a pay rise that month, which would put another dent in the finances. We couldn't back out of that one; everyone was guaranteed it, we'd promised.

It looked really bad. It looked as if we were going to go out of business.

Still, it wasn't all doom and gloom – if I'd learned anything, I'd learned that every cloud had a silver lining, it was always darkest before dawn, glory days are just around the corner, the streets are paved with gold – and, more importantly, Charlie and Catherine were on the other end of the phone. They'd never let me down so far. Whenever I had a problem, I could ring one of them up, or take them to lunch, and they'd always have a great idea about how to fix it, or offer a different perspective that would help me come up with a solution. They were like my fairy friends from over the rainbow, who would come along and plant magic beans in my head that would grow a beanstalk of solutions.

"I'm sorry, Charlie isn't in, he's off for the day meeting some new clients. Can I take a message?"

"Oh. Er, never mind, can I talk to Catherine instead, please?"

"Sorry, she's off all this month. Would you like to leave a message?"

Yes, can you tell them "Eeeeeeeeeeeeeeeeeeeeeeeeeeeee" for me, please...?

"No, that's okay, thanks. Unless..."

"Yes?"

I toyed with the idea of asking a complete stranger if they could help me prevent my company going out of business. I seriously considered it. But then reason prevailed.

"No, thanks for your help."

"Okay, you're welcome, bye."

"Yes. Goodbye."

I put the phone down. My "goodbye" felt and sounded very, very final.

No Charlie. No Catherine. No hope. It looked as if it was all over. We needed a miracle.

I went home early that day. Everyone seemed to know something was wrong, but nobody said anything. They knew that business wasn't as brisk as it could be, but they weren't aware of the full extent of it. I suppose I had to let them know sooner or later, but I didn't have the heart.

When I got home, I made myself a cup of tea. I sat down, and dipped a biscuit into my tea. The biscuit broke, and dropped into the tea, splashing my shirt.

I sighed.

The next day, Yasmin cornered me when I came in.

"Guv," she said. "We know something's up. You need to let us know what the story is. Are our jobs safe? What's going on?"

I looked at her, and tried to smile. It came out all wrong, so I stopped.

"Okay," I said. "Get everyone together in the big conference room at ten."

"Are we okay? Is it going to be okay?"

I looked at her worried face.

"I don't know, Yasmin. I hope so."

It was very quiet in the conference room when I walked in, despite having so many people in there. There was much whispering, but it stopped as soon as I entered the room.

The walk to the top of the room was the longest walk I've ever taken.

Every eye in the room was on me. I would happily have traded places with anyone else in the world at that moment.

"I won't beat around the bush," I said, when I got to the top of the room. "You all know business has been pretty bad lately. Well, it's much worse than usual. We're doing really badly. Barring some sort of miracle, we're probably going to go under in six months."

There was a ripple of panic throughout the room. I pressed on.

"The market has slowed down. The service charge on the building has gone up. The pay rises are due. And the bank isn't exactly being sympathetic. I've tried holding them off for a while, but they've just about lost patience. If we go over our overdraft limit in the next few months, we're dead in the water."

There was silence.

Yasmin put her hand up, shyly. I nodded at her.

"What are we going to do?" she asked.

"I have absolutely no idea. I'm open to suggestions."

We sat there for a while, mulling it over. Yasmin was chatting to some people, and eventually put her hand up again. I smiled at her, and nodded again.

"If it's any help, me and a few others would like to volunteer to miss out on a pay rise. You know, until the next round of increases is due," she said.

I blinked.

"Eh?" I said.

"Well, I can either have a pay rise, and then be out of a job by the end of the year, or skip the pay rise, and stay working here. It's simple, really. We don't want to work somewhere else, go back to the way things used to be. We'll skip the pay rise, thanks."

I was stunned. Yasmin sat down, surprised at all the fuss – everyone was talking quite loudly now, nodding and grinning at each other. Cautiously, I cleared my throat and asked the unaskable.

"Er... does anyone else want to volunteer to skip the pay rise this year?"

Instantly, every hand in the room went up. It was like the scene in *Close Encounters of the Third Kind*, when Truffaut asks the crowd where the sounds and lights came from. It was magical.

It looked as if we had got our miracle.

Without having to pay everyone a pay rise, we managed to just scrape inside our overdraft limit. The bank were impressed. Not impressed enough to throw money at us, but enough not to shut us down.

Everyone did everything they could to save money. We recycled paper – instead of throwing it away if we had printed on one side, we would store it up, and put the other side through the printers. We took it in turns to go through the building before locking up, making sure every computer, every monitor, every single thing was switched off. We made use of one of those cheap international phonecall companies – we needed to keep in touch with overseas clients, but this saved us quite a bit. Everybody came up with ideas to save pennies here, pounds there, and it all helped, every bit.

We pulled through. Just about. But we pulled through.

I went to Charlie and Catherine's place later, when it was over, when we were safe, to thank them.

"Thank us for what?" said Charlie, laughing. "We didn't do anything."

"No," said Catherine. "We weren't even here when you needed us. If you want to thank anyone, you should thank your staff."

"I have, trust me," I admitted. "It is unbelievable though. I still have to pinch myself. That they would come up with an idea like that, and actually volunteer to miss out on a pay rise. Why would they do that?"

"Obvious, really. They enjoy working there. They don't want to have to go somewhere that isn't as nice, so they did what they had to, so that the company would survive."

"Wow. That's pretty crazy stuff. I suppose the better you treat people, the better they work for you."

"Exactly," said Charlie. "That's what's behind all these ideas we've been helping you to figure out. Believing the best, trust, celebrating mistakes, balancing work with home life – what it all comes down to is that people work best when they feel good about themselves."

> People work best when they
> feel good about themselves

"They've proved that," added Catherine. "If things had been like they were in the old days, there's no way they would have volunteered for this. They might have been happy to leave, happy to find some other job. But not now, they like it there. They want to make things work."

"It's so strange," I said. "It's as if it's a completely different company, with different people."

"Well, it is," said Charlie. "The people have changed, and they've changed the company. For the better."

"We came up with another great new thing," I said. "To make sure that everyone stays happy, we do a Happy Check."

Charlie and Catherine looked at each other.

"A Happy Check?" asked Catherine. "What's that, then?"

"Once every three months, everyone fills out a questionnaire which asks things like how happy are you in your job, are you stressed, properly supported, and so on. It's all anonymous, so we can build up an accurate picture of how things are working. Then if anyone has any issues, we sort them out."

"How?" asked Charlie.

"We've set up some action groups to deal with various issues. One group makes sure that we keep a friendly, relaxed atmosphere in the office: plants, toys, that sort of thing. One group comes up with ways to give the customers an even better service. There are quite a few groups, they meet on their own, and it all keeps things running along smoothly."

"Well," said Catherine. "That's a great idea. Maybe we should try that, Charlie?"

Charlie nodded.

"Looks like we've both got stuff we can learn from you too. Well done, Howard, I knew you had it in you."

I got up to leave, after one final round of thanks. Just as I was leaving, I remembered that I still had a problem – we were doing okay, but we were having trouble getting more clients. I asked Charlie what he thought I should do.

"I don't know," he said.

"You don't know? But – but you always know!" I spluttered.

"Not always. We're not perfect here, you know. We don't get it right all the time. There are still quite a few things we need to fix, things that don't work properly. But we're getting there. We're working on them. We don't know how to get more clients right now, the market isn't too strong, as you know."

"So what are you going to do, then?"

Charlie shrugged. "I don't know. I'm going to ask the staff. They usually have the best ideas."

Then he winked, and strolled off.

He was full of surprises, that guy.

.

- 🐾 People work best when they feel good about themselves
- 🐾 How would your organisation be different if management focused on making people feel good?"
- 🐾 Ask your people for ideas – they may know how things work better than you!

Epilogue

He should have been having fun. He really should. Sun, sand, sea, his wife, his kids, a beautiful villa right on the beach, just down from a bar that did great lobster – he should have been having the time of his life.

But he wasn't.

He looked about my age, but there the resemblance ended. His wife was sitting on the beach, trying to relax and enjoy herself; his three kids were playing with a beachball; but he was sitting with a laptop computer connected to a mobile phone, and swearing a lot.

I, on the other hand, was perfectly relaxed. I had helped my kids build a huge, elaborate sandcastle that was promptly washed away by the tide as soon as the last bucket load of sand went in place. Later on we'd build another one. The important thing about sandcastles is not the finished product, it's the fun you have making it – and emptying buckets of water over each other, of course.

The kids were now snoozing in the shade, my wife was sunning herself, and I was just stretched out, enjoying myself in the peace and quiet.

Quiet, that is, except for the guy with his laptop, who was making a lot of noise. He was stabbing at the keys as if he was trying to win a prize at a fairground "test your strength" machine. For some reason, the combination of violence, swearing, sun, sand and moisture wasn't having a beneficial effect on the laptop.

I watched him for a while, amused. It could almost have been me a year or two ago.

Eventually the laptop committed one crime too many. The man grabbed the mobile phone, which was still connected to it, and swung it around his head like that Olympic event with the big ball on a string. When he let go with a roar of triumph, the phone and laptop sailed out into the sea, and plopped out of sight.

I strolled over to him.

"Are you okay?" I asked. "Only you look a bit stressed."

"What do you know about stress?" he snapped.

"Quite a bit actually," I replied. "Let me tell you a story..."

The End

Acknowledgements

This book is based on our experience at the London-based training company Happy Ltd. However many of the concepts are borrowed from other companies and individuals. We beg, steal and borrow ideas from wherever we can and encourage you to do the same.

The biggest influence on the company is probably *Maverick*, a book by Ricardo Semler. It describes how Ricardo took over a Brazilian manufacturing company called Semco from his father, and transformed it into a business based on trust. Every new recruit at Happy gets a copy and we have given away over five hundred in total. We recommend you buy it. Now!

We think we first came across the concept "Hire for attitude, train for skill" in Tom Peters' writings, though many companies quote it and SouthWest Airlines may have been the first company to proclaim it.

"Without information you cannot take responsibility. With information you cannot avoid taking responsibility": this statement originates from Jan Carlssen of SAS Airlines.

For more on building on people's strengths, get hold of *Now Discover Your Strengths* by Marcus Buckingham. This outlines the "Strengthfinder" philosophy, and includes a free online survey to identify your five key strengths.

Concepts such as "People work best when they feel good about themselves", "Celebrate mistakes" and "Always believe the best" originate from Re-Evaluation Counselling. Find out more at www.rc.org.

Other key influences include everybody who works, or has ever worked, at Happy. They are a great bunch of people.

A special thanks to Jenny Boyce of Vertigo Communications, whose knowledge of the publishing world, and considerable patience, made this book possible. If you want to publish a book, she is a great place to start.

Contacting the Authors

This story is fictional. Many people have asked me questions like "Where was the beach?" I'm afraid there was no beach. That was James's way of bringing the story to life.

But the principles that Howard employs in the book to turn his business round are very real and in use, in one way or another, in our business and in many organisations that we have worked with.

We are not couriers but trainers. I set up the company as Happy Computers, making learning about IT a fun and involving experience. Over the years we branched out and created Happy People, which helps organisations create great workplaces.

Please feel free to contact us, to chat, to subscribe to the happy@work email newsletter or to employ us to help turn your organisation into one based on trust and freedom.

Happy Ltd
40 Adler Street
London
E1 1EE
020 7375 7300
happy@happy.co.uk
www.happy-people.co.uk

Or contact me directly on 07870 682442 or henry@happy.co.uk. Yes, that is my personal mobile and my personal email address.

Henry Stewart
Chief Executive, Happy Ltd